Spiritual Journal

"If you are too busy to spend time with God, you are busier than He intends you to be."

Name _____

Address _____

_____ Tel: _____

Date: From _____ To _____

International Evangelism Association,
P.O. Box 6883,
Fort Worth, Texas 76115, USA.
Tel: 817 926 8465.

Spiritual Journal

Billie Hanks Jr. with

Billy Beacham

WORD PUBLISHING

Word (UK) Ltd
Milton Keynes, England

WORD BOOKS
Waco, Texas, USA
WORD AUSTRALIA
Heathmont, Victoria, Australia
SUNDAY SCHOOL CENTRE WHOLESALE
Salt River, South Africa
ALBY COMMERCIAL ENTERPRISES PTE LTD
Balmoral Road, Singapore
CONCORDE DISTRIBUTORS LTD
Havelock North, New Zealand
CROSS (HK) CO
Hong Kong

SPIRITUAL JOURNAL

Copyright © 1981 International Evangelism Association

First published in the USA by Word Incorporated, Waco, Texas

This edition © 1988 Word (UK) Ltd.

ISBN 0–85009–146–2

Typesetting by Suripace Ltd, Milton Keynes.
Reproduced, printed and bound in Great Britain for Word (UK) Ltd
by Cox and Wyman Ltd, Reading.

ABOUT THE AUTHORS

Dr. Billie Hanks, Jr. serves as the president of International Evangelism Association in Fort Worth, Texas. He has taught and written widely on the disciplines of spiritual growth, and his books *Everyday Evangelism* and *If You Love Me* are published by Word UK.

As a guest of the Billy Graham Evangelistic Association, Dr. Hanks came to Britain for the Earls Court Crusade in 1966. He is dedicated to the training of men and women who are called to Christian service and is known for his emphasis on personal follow-up and discipleship. The *Spiritual Journal* is North America's best-selling book of its kind and is also published in the Korean, Chinese and Danish languages.

Dr. Hanks' wife Ruth and daughters Heidi and Heather enjoy an active life with him in Texas. Their family hobbies include writing music, sailing, water-skiing and fishing.

Rev. Bill Beacham is president of Student Discipleship Ministries, also based in Fort Worth. His work involves writing youth curriculum for discipleship training in churches. He also maintains a full speaking schedule. Each year twenty-five to forty thousand students study one or more of his courses.

Rev. Beacham and his wife Tracye have one son named Billy. Their favourite family activities include water-skiing and boating.

A PERSONAL WORD FROM DR. BILLIE HANKS, JR.

I pray that this new **Spiritual Journal** will find a natural and exciting place in your walk with Jesus Christ. My own journals have been constant companions through the years. Many of my fondest memories and deepest insights from the Lord are to be found in their pages. If those insights were ever lost, no amount of money could replace them. Their value is not of the kind that money can buy.

When the Lord opens a passage in the Bible to your understanding or teaches you some important lesson through the living of life, you are being entrusted with a pearl of great worth. How should you treat such a pearl? For years, I wasted mine. I forgot the good sermons I heard. I lost the fruit of my quiet times. I left behind the priceless insights gained from my spiritual successes and failures.

One day, God used Matthew 7:6 to convict me! *"Give not that which is holy unto the dogs, neither cast ye your pearls before swine."* He made me see that I was no more mature than the foolish Pharisees, who failed to value that which was holy. Like the dogs and the swine of Jesus' parable, I was wasting and abusing His precious pearls!

Why my life felt empty

God brought me to see *why* my life felt empty so much of the time. Why should He bless me, when I took His love and fellowship so lightly? Why should I expect Him to teach me? He knew I would only look forward to the moment of inspiration – never really intending to meditate on my new-found truths or apply them in my daily life.

I began to think I could never break the cycle of spiritual ups and downs. Steady growth seemed impossible! Then slowly but surely things began to change. An older Christian began to disciple me, much as Paul helped young Timothy. He showed me the importance of discipline and taught me how to enjoy consistent fellowship with Christ. Life took on a wonderful new dimension!

A "Quiet Time" made the difference

Like so many other Christians, I was delightfully surprised to discover the great difference a daily "quiet time" could make. I learned firsthand what Moses meant in Psalm 90:14, *"O satisfy us in the morning with Thy lovingkindness, that we may sing for joy and be glad all our days"* (NAS). I experienced His steadfast love in the mornings, and I began to grow.

As time passed, it became natural for me to take notes on my quiet times and the sermons I heard at church. Writing on the back of my bulletin had never been satisfactory, so I began carrying a journal. It grew as I grew, and finally it developed into the **Spiritual Journal** which exists today.

As you begin to use the Quiet Time section, it will also find a special place of importance in your life. When this happens, carefully reserve those special times for fellowship – not for work! Your first objective is simply to read your Bible to know God better and experience the joy of His presence.

Be still, as you begin your quiet time. Prepare your heart to listen, and read the Bible expecting a blessing. God will show you more of Himself and His will for your life as He finds that you are *teachable*. Your Quiet Time section is designed to help you grow in that life-changing process. Maturing in Christ comes as the result of our desire to be consistent. Jesus said, *"If ye continue in My Word, then are ye My disciples indeed"* (John 8:31).

Learning to share

As you enjoy the blessings of Bible reading, prayer, Scripture memory and note taking, remember to *share* what you are learning with others. When Jesus called Andrew and Peter, He said, *"Follow Me, and I will make you become fishers of men"* (Mark 1:17, NAS). The authenticating mark of true discipleship is the love that causes us to witness. Our commission is to reach out. Jesus said, *"Make disciples of all nations . . . teaching them to observe all that I have commanded you; and lo, I am with you always . . ."* (Matthew 28:19-20, NAS).

Jesus has not changed! He is still calling men and women to be His committed disciples, not merely His converts. In that awareness, may we take seriously this clear call to be disciplined followers and walk in the joy of His abundant life.

May God bless you and give you real fulfillment as you get involved in personal growth and ministry. I pray that this spiritual aid will prove to be a consistent and inspiring part of your Christian life. Let's covenant together to seek to be fully "usable".

Yours in that expectation,

Billie Hanks, Jr.

"As you therefore have received Christ Jesus the Lord, so walk in Him" (Colossians 2:6, NAS).

CONTENTS

Quiet Time
Section 1

HOW TO USE THE QUIET TIME SECTION

"Be still and know that I am God . . ." (Psalm 46:10a, KJV)

This page gives a simple outline for spending a quarter of an hour with God each day. It can be expanded on as you wish.

1. BEGIN YOUR 15-MINUTE QUIET TIME WITH PRAYER (30 seconds)

   This should be a *brief prayer* for understanding as you prepare to read God's Word.

2. PAUSE FOR MEDITATION (30 seconds)

   Meditate on the meaning of your selected memory verse for the week. Repeat it *out loud* several times, emphasizing the key words which make it meaningful. Seek to find verses that apply to your own spiritual growth. (There is space at the top of each Quiet Time page for your new memory verse.)

3. READ THE SCRIPTURES (5 minutes)

   You may choose to use the Bible Reading Plan included in your **Journal** (P.202); however, the Quiet Time Section will also work in conjunction with *any other* plan you select. Regardless of the approach you are led to take, remember that consistency and expectancy are the secrets to spiritual growth in personal devotions.

4. RECORD INSIGHTS AND MAKE PERSONAL APPLICATION (3 minutes)

   Think about the meaning of what you read. NOTE: In the example on page 13, you will see several ways you can use symbols to identify and emphasize items which you wish to recall.

   To help make a personal application, you might ask these questions (they can be remembered by the acrostic SPACE):*

Is there a . . .	**Sin** for me to confess?
	Promise for me to claim?
	Attitude for me to change?
	Command for me to obey?
	Example for me to follow?

   *Used by permission, Rick Warren.

   WRITE OUT your thoughts and seek to make your applications PERSONAL, SPECIFIC and MEASURABLE.

5. SPEND TIME IN PRAYER (2 minutes)

   Ask God to guide you throughout the day and to provide opportunities for you to apply what you have learned during your Quiet Time. Instructions for five important aspects of prayer are on the following pages.

6. REVIEW MEMORY VERSES (4 minutes)

   Review your verses from previous weeks, using the special *Review Section* at the top of your Quiet Time page.

   END YOUR QUIET TIME, BUT CONTINUE THE DAY IN PRAYER.

Scripture Memory Review	Date	Jan 7-13

Matt. 6:33
Josh. 1:8
Jer. 33:3
Psa. 46:10
Eph: 6:11

S	M	T	W	T	F	S
☑	☑	☑	☐	☐	☐	☐

Memory Verse for the Week
1 Peter 1:15 *"But like the Holy One who called you, be holy yourselves also in all your behaviour."*

QUIET TIME

Scriptural Insight	Prayer

SUNDAY

1 Peter 1:13 *"Gird your minds for action"* Don't just slide into the day. Meet it positively.
☆ vs. 14 *"former lusts"* Don't fall into the same old sin traps.
m vs. 15 Holiness is our objective.
x 1 Thess. 4:7 *". . . live a holy life."*

P Father, help my mind to stay centred on You today.

C Forgive me for thinking impure thoughts yesterday. Please continue to purify my mind.

Application:
I will prepare my mind for Christ-centred thoughts today by meditating on my Quiet Time insights while driving to work rather than listening to the radio.

MONDAY

➤ 1 Peter 2:13 *"Submit . . . to every human institution"* We are to be law-abiding and submissive to those in authority.
☆ vs 21 *"Christ also suffered . . . leaving an example"* Suffering is evidently part of becoming like our Lord.

C Forgive me for consistently breaking the speed limits.

T Lord, thank You for reminding me that you are not unfamiliar with pain and can identify fully with the times when my body hurts.

Application:
As from today, I will begin driving within the speed limits. Since most of my speeding comes from running late, I will need to be better organised.

TUESDAY

☆ 1 Peter 3:15 *"always being ready to make a defence"* I must be prepared to witness on any occasion. This desire will flow out of Christ being Lord in my life.

P Lord, you are aware of my burden for Sam. The last time we talked I couldn't answer his questions. Please enable me to be prepared for the next opportunity.

Application:
Tonight I will do some reading which will help me answer Sam next time.

☆	my meditation for today	A	Adoration
➤	further study needed	C	Confession
x	cross reference	T	Thanksgiving
m	verse(s) to memorize	P	Petition

SCRIPTURE MEMORY

"Thy word have I hid in mine heart, that I might not sin against thee."
(Psalm 119:11, KJV)

Normally, references are more easily forgotten than verses. Your review system helps overcome this problem by including spaces for six abbreviated references. Rewrite your references each Sunday morning during your Quiet Time. Quote the references out loud *before* and *after* saying each verse as you review it.

A verse is not truly memorized until you *cannot forget it*. Merely learning a verse is not your spiritual objective – live with the verse until it saturates your mind and affects the way you think and act. Good review is the basis for good meditation, and spiritual meditation produces the kind of thinking that builds a godly life. (Philippians 4:8)

Scripture memory requires consistency. Hold yourself accountable by checking the boxes provided by each reference. By simply reviewing each verse for six weeks, you will make a major step toward committing it to memory

Remember the admonition of Philippians 4:13: *"I can do all things through Christ which strengtheneth me." (KJV)* This includes hiding God's Word in your heart!

In this illustration you have already memorized five verses and said them out loud three times during the week.

You are now learning Philippians 4:13.

SAMPLE

Scripture Memory Review Matt. 6:33	Date_____ Jan. 7-13
Josh. 1:8	Memory Verse for the Week
Jer. 33:3	Philippians 4:13 *"I can do all things through Christ*
Psa. 46:10	*which strengtheneth me."*
Eph. 6:11	
S M T W T F S ☑ ☑ ☑ ☐ ☐ ☐ ☐	

FIVE ASPECTS OF PRAYER

1 ADORATION

(Praising God for Who He is)

"I will bless the Lord at all times; His praise shall continually be in my mouth." (Psalm 34:1, NAS)

There is no better way to *begin* a time of prayer than by expressing praise to God! Praise is the most important element of prayer, and it is probably one of the most neglected. In a prayer of adoration, you express your deep feelings toward God in response to His love, wisdom, presence, power, knowledge, grace, holiness, greatness and His other divine attributes. This kind of prayer will always be an occasion for joy!

As you enrol in the school of prayer, remember this important lesson: Our *adoration* must be reserved for God, not for projects, ministries or works done in His name. When you are in His will, the desire to praise Him will come naturally.

PRAISING GOD IN ADORATION

To help you experience this valuable form of prayer, several choice passages have been listed below.

MAJESTY – 1 Chron. 29:11, Psa. 8:9, Job 37:22
HOLINESS – Ex. 15:11, Isa. 6:3, 1 Pet. 1:14-16

The symbol "A" for "Adoration" is used in the code provided in the daily Quiet Time prayer section. As you read, you will find many verses which describe God's divine attributes. Make them the subject of your prayer.

	Scriptural Insight	Prayer
	➤ 1 Chron. 29:1-2 Although the temple	A Father, I join David this morning in
	bore Solomon's name, David actually	saying that you are the very essence of
S	provided the wealth of materials needed	greatness, power, glory, and victory.
A	for its construction.	Everything everywhere belongs to
M	☆ v. 3 & 9 David gave with joy!	You – including me.
P	v. 11 In his prayer of adoration he	
L	praised God for his greatness.	
E		

Application:
I will meditate throughout the day upon who God really is, and I will tell Him how proud I am to be His child.

☆	my meditation for today	A	Adoration
➤	further study needed	C	Confession
x	cross reference	T	Thanksgiving
m	verse(s) to memorize	P	Petition

2 CONFESSION
(Agreeing with God about your Sin)

"If we confess our sins, He is faithful and righteous to forgive us our sins and to cleanse us from all unrighteousness." (1 John 1:9, NAS)

Receiving God's gift of forgiveness is part of the miracle that occurs in a person's life when he accepts Christ as his Saviour. Choosing to accept this gift, made possible through the cross, establishes one's eternal *relationship* with God; however, it is our prayer life and obedience that maintain our *fellowship* with Him on a day-to-day basis.

Jesus said, *"If you love Me, you will keep My commandments"* (John 14:15, NAS). When we make self-centred and sinful decisions, our relationship with God remains the same, but the quality of our fellowship is strained. It is *confession* that restores the privilege of that wonderful fellowship.

HOW TO PRACTISE CONFESSION

As you use the daily Quiet Time portion of your **Journal**, note the single "C", which stands for "confession". A sincere prayer of confession will normally demand that a practical application be made.

Both sin and righteousness are the result of personal decisions, so *confession* that is based upon *genuine repentance* will be proved by a *change* in your daily life. For this reason, your greatest spiritual victories will normally come as the result of this honest, cleansing kind of prayer.

Your confession and repentance need to be *specific*.

	Scriptural Insight	Prayer
S	Eph. 5:15b-16 *"wise, making the most of your time . . ."* Wise people use their time well!	C Lord, I have been wasting a lot of time watching T.V. lately. These are hours I could have spent in Bible reading, prayer
A **M** **P** **L** **E**	☆ vs. 17:20 The secret of using my time well is being controlled by the Holy Spirit.	or service. Please forgive my misplaced attention.

Application:
I will reduce my T.V. viewing to five hours per week.

☆	my meditation for today	A	Adoration
➜	further study needed	C	Confession
x	cross reference	T	Thanksgiving
m	verse(s) to memorize	P	Petition

3 THANKSGIVING

(Expressing gratitude to God for What He Has Done)

"In everything give thanks; for this is God's will for you in Christ Jesus." (1 Thessalonians 5:18, NAS)

The average Christian probably spends too *much* time *asking* and too *little* time *thanking*.

Paul's admonition to *"give thanks in everything"* reflects the maturity of his Christian life. He had been shipwrecked, beaten, hungry, severely criticized and imprisoned – yet he could honestly write those words. Why? Because his heart was filled with gratitude! He expressed it like this:

"But whatever things were gain to me, those things I have counted as loss for the sake of Christ. More than that, I count all things to be loss in the view of the surpassing value of knowing Christ Jesus my Lord . . ." (Philippians 3:7-8, NAS)

Prayer provides the opportunity to express our deepest emotions and feelings to God. How long has it been since your heart was overwhelmed with a sense of gratitude?

OFFERING THANKSGIVING IN PRAYER

As you use the Quiet Time section of your **Journal**, simply express the natural appreciation in your heart. To indicate your thanksgiving, write "T" in the margin as your code. Begin thanking God for the things in life which you may have taken for granted. Here are some practical examples:

		Scriptural Insight		Prayer
S	m	Titus 2:7 *"In all things show yourself to be*	T	Lord, as I look back over the years I
		an example of good deeds . . ." The		want to thank You for Sunday School
A		ministry of example may be the most		teachers, friends and family members
M		important outreach I can have.		who have been good examples for
P		vs. 2-3 Both older men and women are to		me to follow.
L		live out the Christian faith in a way		
E		attractive to younger believers.		

Application:
I will write a thankyou note to Mrs. Dixon and let her know how much her life has meant to me. I will seek to make my own life a positive example to others.

☆	my meditation for today	A	Adoration
➤	further study needed	C	Confession
x	cross reference	T	Thanksgiving
m	verse(s) to memorize	P	Petition

4 PETITION

(Praying for Your Personal Needs)

"Until now you have asked for nothing in My name; ask, and you will receive, that your joy may be made full." (John 16:24, NAS)

On a day-to-day basis, most of your petitions will deal with small-scale problems, decisions and opportunities. That is natural, so don't consider your needs beneath God's interest. Remember, Jesus said the Father even knows when a sparrow falls!

Perhaps no verse in the New Testament is as helpful with regard to prayers of petition as John 14:13, in which Jesus said, *"And whatsoever ye shall ask in my name, that will I do, that the Father may be glorified in the Son."* (KJV)

In both large and small requests, the question should always be, "Is my prayer the kind that will *glorify* my heavenly Father?"

Pray about everything, and try not to confuse your *needs* with your *wants*. By faith, be prepared to *praise* Him for a *"yes"* or a *"no"* when He answers your petition. He knows your need, even before you ask. His promise is wonderfully understandable – *"Seek ye first the kingdom of God, and His righteousness; and all these things shall be added unto you."* (Matthew 6:33, KJV)

BRINGING PETITIONS TO GOD

As you learn to make your requests using the Quiet Time portion of your **Journal**, indicate your petitions with the symbol "P".

	Scriptural Insight		Prayer
S **A** **M** **P** **L** **E**	➤ Titus 1:7-9 The attributes for spiritual leadership are available to everyone, because they are character qualities that can be developed rather than human talents. This is good news!	P	Father, I want very much to have a godly character, so I can be used by You in ministry. Please prepare me for service any way, any time, anywhere.

Application:
This week I will ask Ruth Jones and Bill Smith what they did to develop the godly character which is so obvious in their lives.

☆	my meditation for today	A	Adoration
➤	further study needed	C	Confession
x	cross reference	T	Thanksgiving
m	verse(s) to memorize	P	Petition

5 INTERCESSION

(Praying for the Needs of Others)

". . . . far be it from me that I should sin against the Lord by ceasing to pray for you." (1 Samuel 12:23, NAS)

When Christ enters our lives, it becomes our spontaneous desire to seek God's blessings for those around us. This is called "intercession".

It would probably be safe to say that the most consistent intercessory praying which we do focuses on the spiritual needs of relative, friends and neighbours. Many of those we intercede for are lost. Others are Christians living beneath the resources and privileges freely available to God's children. In each of these instances, intercessory prayer is a ministry of love.

Through intercession, any Christian can be mightily used by God to affect the cause of evangelism worldwide. Whatever our physical condition, we can all be part of God's powerful army of prayer. Jesus said to His disciples, *"If you abide in Me, and My words abide in you, ask whatever you wish, and it shall be done for you."* (John 15:7, NAS)

QUIET TIME

INTERCEDING FOR OTHERS

List the names of *individuals* and *ministries* that you want to pray for. When possible, present their needs to God by name. Pray for them exactly as you would want them to pray for you.

The following pages provide for each day of the week. The example below shows how to use the code at the bottom of the Intercession pages:

	NAME	SPECIFIC REQUEST
S **A** **M** **P** **L** **E**	N John	Please show him what drinking will do to his life.
	F Dad	Give him wisdom in the job decision he is making.
	C Jim	Help him as he shares Christ with his grandmother.

F	Family	- immediate family and other relatives
M	Ministries	- church leaders, church services, missionaries and organizations
C	Close Friends	- relationships outside my immediate family
N	Non-Christian Friends	- those who have not yet come to know Christ
G	Government	- local and national officials and agencies

INTERCESSION

	NAME	SPECIFIC REQUEST
D A I L Y		
S U N D A Y		

F	Family	- immediate family and other relatives
M	Ministries	- church leaders, church services, missionaries and organizations
C	Close Friends	- relationships outside my immediate family
N	Non-Christian Friends	- those who have not yet come to know Christ
G	Government	- local and national officials and agencies

INTERCESSION

	NAME	SPECIFIC REQUEST	
M O N D A Y			*QUIET TIME*
T U E S D A Y			

F	Family	- immediate family and other relatives
M	Ministries	- church leaders, church services, missionaries and organizations
C	Close Friends	- relationships outside my immediate family
N	Non-Christian Friends	- those who have not yet come to know Christ
G	Government	- local and national officials and agencies

INTERCESSION

NAME	SPECIFIC REQUEST
WEDNESDAY	
THURSDAY	

F	Family	- immediate family and other relatives
M	Ministries	- church leaders, church services, missionaries and organizations
C	Close Friends	- relationships outside my immediate family
N	Non-Christian Friends	- those who have not yet come to know Christ
G	Government	- local and national officials and agencies

INTERCESSION

	NAME	SPECIFIC REQUEST	
F R I D A Y			*QUIET TIME*
S A T U R D A Y			

F	Family	- immediate family and other relatives
M	Ministries	- church leaders, church services, missionaries and organizations
C	Close Friends	- relationships outside my immediate family
N	Non-Christian Friends	- those who have not yet come to know Christ
G	Government	- local and national officials and agencies

SPECIAL PRAYER

DATE	PRAYER	DATE ANSWERED

SPECIAL PRAYER

DATE	PRAYER	DATE ANSWERED

QUIET TIME

SPECIAL PRAYER

DATE	PRAYER	DATE ANSWERED

SPECIAL PRAYER

DATE	PRAYER	DATE ANSWERED	
			QUIET TIME

Scriptural Insights and Prayer

Scripture Memory Review	Date_____
_____	Memory Verse for the Week
_____	_____
_____	_____
_____	_____
S M T W T F S ☐ ☐ ☐ ☐ ☐ ☐ ☐	_____

	Scriptural Insight	Prayer
S U N D A Y	_____ _____ _____ _____ _____ _____	_____ _____ _____ _____ _____ _____
	Application:	
M O N D A Y	_____ _____ _____ _____ _____ _____	_____ _____ _____ _____ _____ _____
	Application:	
T U E S D A Y	_____ _____ _____ _____ _____ _____	_____ _____ _____ _____ _____ _____
	Application:	

☆	my meditation for today	A	Adoration
➤	further study needed	C	Confession
x	cross reference	T	Thanksgiving
m	verse(s) to memorize	P	Petition

QUIET TIME

Week 1 ....

WEDNESDAY

Application:

THURSDAY

Application:

FRIDAY

Application:

SATURDAY

Application:

Scriptural Insights and Prayer

<table>
<tr><td colspan="2">Scripture Memory Review

</td><td colspan="2">Date_____
Memory Verse for the Week

</td></tr>
<tr><td colspan="2">S M T W T F S
☐ ☐ ☐ ☐ ☐ ☐ ☐</td><td colspan="2"></td></tr>
</table>

	Scriptural Insight	Prayer
S U N D A Y		
	Application:	
M O N D A Y		
	Application:	
T U E S D A Y		
	Application:	

☆ my meditation for today	A Adoration
➤ further study needed	C Confession
x cross reference	T Thanksgiving
m verse(s) to memorize	P Petition

WEDNESDAY

Application:

THURSDAY

Application:

FRIDAY

Application:

SATURDAY

Application:

QUIET TIME

Week 2

Scriptural Insights and Prayer

Scripture Memory Review	Date_____
_____	Memory Verse for the Week
_____	_____
_____	_____
_____	_____
S M T W T F S	_____
☐ ☐ ☐ ☐ ☐ ☐ ☐	_____

	Scriptural Insight	Prayer
S U N D A Y		
	Application:	
M O N D A Y		
	Application:	
T U E S D A Y		
	Application:	

☆	my meditation for today	A	Adoration
➤	further study needed	C	Confession
x	cross reference	T	Thanksgiving
m	verse(s) to memorize	P	Petition

WEDNESDAY

Application:

THURSDAY

Application:

FRIDAY

Application:

SATURDAY

Application:

QUIET TIME

Week 3

Scriptural Insights and Prayer

Scripture Memory Review	Date_____
_____	Memory Verse for the Week
_____	_____
_____	_____
_____	_____
S M T W T F S	_____
☐ ☐ ☐ ☐ ☐ ☐ ☐	_____

	Scriptural Insight	Prayer

S U N D A Y

Scriptural Insight / Prayer

Application:

M O N D A Y

Scriptural Insight / Prayer

Application:

T U E S D A Y

Scriptural Insight / Prayer

Application:

☆	my meditation for today	A	Adoration
➤	further study needed	C	Confession
x	cross reference	T	Thanksgiving
m	verse(s) to memorize	P	Petition

-34-

QUIET TIME

Week 4

WEDNESDAY

Application:

THURSDAY

Application:

FRIDAY

Application:

SATURDAY

Application:

Scriptural Insights and Prayer

Scripture Memory Review	Date_____
_____	Memory Verse for the Week
_____	_____
_____	_____
_____	_____
S M T W T F S	_____
☐ ☐ ☐ ☐ ☐ ☐ ☐	_____

Scriptural Insight	Prayer

S U N D A Y

Application:

M O N D A Y

Application:

T U E S D A Y

Application:

☆	my meditation for today	A	Adoration
➤	further study needed	C	Confession
x	cross reference	T	Thanksgiving
m	verse(s) to memorize	P	Petition

QUIET TIME

Week 5 ....

WEDNESDAY

_____
_____
_____
_____
_____
_____

Application:
_____
_____
_____

THURSDAY

_____
_____
_____
_____
_____
_____

Application:
_____
_____
_____

FRIDAY

_____
_____
_____
_____
_____
_____

Application:
_____
_____
_____

SATURDAY

_____
_____
_____
_____
_____
_____

Application:
_____
_____
_____

Scriptural Insights and Prayer

Scripture Memory Review	Date_____
_____	Memory Verse for the Week
_____	_____
_____	_____
_____	_____
S M T W T F S	_____
☐ ☐ ☐ ☐ ☐ ☐ ☐	_____

	Scriptural Insight	Prayer
S U N D A Y	_____ _____ _____ _____ _____ _____	_____ _____ _____ _____ _____ _____
	Application:	
M O N D A Y	_____ _____ _____ _____ _____ _____	_____ _____ _____ _____ _____ _____
	Application:	
T U E S D A Y	_____ _____ _____ _____ _____ _____	_____ _____ _____ _____ _____ _____
	Application:	

☆	my meditation for today	A	Adoration
➤	further study needed	C	Confession
x	cross reference	T	Thanksgiving
m	verse(s) to memorize	P	Petition

QUIET TIME

Week 6

WEDNESDAY

Application:

THURSDAY

Application:

FRIDAY

Application:

SATURDAY

Application:

Scriptural Insights and Prayer

Scripture Memory Review	Date_____
_____	Memory Verse for the Week
_____	_____
_____	_____
_____	_____
S M T W T F S	_____
☐ ☐ ☐ ☐ ☐ ☐ ☐	_____

	Scriptural Insight	Prayer
S U N D A Y	_____ _____ _____ _____ _____ _____ _____	_____ _____ _____ _____ _____ _____
	Application:	
M O N D A Y	_____ _____ _____ _____ _____ _____	_____ _____ _____ _____ _____ _____
	Application:	
T U E S D A Y	_____ _____ _____ _____ _____ _____	_____ _____ _____ _____ _____ _____
	Application:	

☆	my meditation for today	A	Adoration
➤	further study needed	C	Confession
x	cross reference	T	Thanksgiving
m	verse(s) to memorize	P	Petition

QUIET TIME

Week 7 ....

WEDNESDAY

Application:

THURSDAY

Application:

FRIDAY

Application:

SATURDAY

Application:

Scriptural Insights and Prayer

Scripture Memory Review	Date_____
_____	Memory Verse for the Week
_____	_____
_____	_____
_____	_____
S M T W T F S ☐ ☐ ☐ ☐ ☐ ☐ ☐	_____

Scriptural Insight	Prayer

SUNDAY

Scriptural Insight
_____
_____
_____
_____
_____

Prayer
_____
_____
_____
_____
_____

Application:
_____
_____

MONDAY

_____
_____
_____
_____
_____

_____
_____
_____
_____
_____

Application:
_____
_____

TUESDAY

_____
_____
_____
_____
_____

_____
_____
_____
_____
_____

Application:
_____
_____

☆	my meditation for today	A	Adoration
➤	further study needed	C	Confession
x	cross reference	T	Thanksgiving
m	verse(s) to memorize	P	Petition

WEDNESDAY

Application:

THURSDAY

Application:

FRIDAY

Application:

SATURDAY

Application:

Scriptural Insights and Prayer

Scripture Memory Review	Date_____
_____	Memory Verse for the Week
_____	_____
_____	_____
_____	_____
S M T W T F S	_____
☐ ☐ ☐ ☐ ☐ ☐ ☐	_____

	Scriptural Insight	Prayer
S U N D A Y		
	Application:	
M O N D A Y		
	Application:	
T U E S D A Y		
	Application:	

☆ my meditation for today	A Adoration
➤ further study needed	C Confession
x cross reference	T Thanksgiving
m verse(s) to memorize	P Petition

-44-

WEDNESDAY

Application:

THURSDAY

Application:

FRIDAY

Application:

SATURDAY

Application:

Scriptural Insights and Prayer

Scripture Memory Review	Date_____
_____	Memory Verse for the Week
_____	_____
_____	_____
_____	_____
S M T W T F S	_____
□ □ □ □ □ □ □	_____

	Scriptural Insight	Prayer

SUNDAY

Application:

MONDAY

Application:

TUESDAY

Application:

☆ my meditation for today	A Adoration
➤ further study needed	C Confession
x cross reference	T Thanksgiving
m verse(s) to memorize	P Petition

WEDNESDAY

Application:

THURSDAY

Application:

FRIDAY

Application:

SATURDAY

Application:

Scriptural Insights and Prayer

Scripture Memory Review	Date_____
_____	Memory Verse for the Week
_____	_____
_____	_____
_____	_____
S M T W T F S	_____
☐ ☐ ☐ ☐ ☐ ☐ ☐	_____

Scriptural Insight   Prayer

SUNDAY

Application:

MONDAY

Application:

TUESDAY

Application:

☆	my meditation for today	A	Adoration
➤	further study needed	C	Confession
x	cross reference	T	Thanksgiving
m	verse(s) to memorize	P	Petition

WEDNESDAY

Application:

THURSDAY

Application:

FRIDAY

Application:

SATURDAY

Application:

Scriptural Insights and Prayer

Scripture Memory Review	Date_____
_____	Memory Verse for the Week
_____	_____
_____	_____
_____	_____
S M T W T F S ☐ ☐ ☐ ☐ ☐ ☐ ☐	_____

	Scriptural Insight	Prayer
S U N D A Y		
	Application:	
M O N D A Y		
	Application:	
T U E S D A Y		
	Application:	

☆	my meditation for today	A	Adoration
➤	further study needed	C	Confession
x	cross reference	T	Thanksgiving
m	verse(s) to memorize	P	Petition

WEDNESDAY

Application:

THURSDAY

Application:

FRIDAY

Application:

SATURDAY

Application:

QUIET TIME

Week 12 ....

Scriptural Insights and Prayer

Scripture Memory Review	Date_____
_____	Memory Verse for the Week
_____	_____
_____	_____
_____	_____
S M T W T F S	_____
☐ ☐ ☐ ☐ ☐ ☐ ☐	_____

	Scriptural Insight	Prayer
S U N D A Y	_____	_____
	Application:	
M O N D A Y	_____	_____
	Application:	
T U E S D A Y	_____	_____
	Application:	

☆	my meditation for today	A	Adoration
➤	further study needed	C	Confession
x	cross reference	T	Thanksgiving
m	verse(s) to memorize	P	Petition

QUIET TIME

Week 13 ....

WEDNESDAY

Application:

THURSDAY

Application:

FRIDAY

Application:

SATURDAY

Application:

Scriptural Insights and Prayer

Scripture Memory Review	Date_____
_____	Memory Verse for the Week
_____	_____
_____	_____
_____	_____
S M T W T F S	_____
☐ ☐ ☐ ☐ ☐ ☐ ☐	_____

	Scriptural Insight	Prayer
S U N D A Y		
	Application:	
M O N D A Y		
	Application:	
T U E S D A Y		
	Application:	

☆	my meditation for today	A	Adoration
➜	further study needed	C	Confession
x	cross reference	T	Thanksgiving
m	verse(s) to memorize	P	Petition

WEDNESDAY

Application:

THURSDAY

Application:

FRIDAY

Application:

SATURDAY

Application:

Scriptural Insights and Prayer

Scripture Memory Review	Date_____
_____	Memory Verse for the Week
_____	_____
_____	_____
_____	_____
S M T W T F S □ □ □ □ □ □ □	_____

Scriptural Insight	Prayer

SUNDAY

Scriptural Insight
_____
_____
_____
_____
_____
_____

Prayer
_____
_____
_____
_____
_____
_____

Application:
_____
_____

MONDAY

Scriptural Insight
_____
_____
_____
_____
_____
_____

Prayer
_____
_____
_____
_____
_____
_____

Application:
_____
_____

TUESDAY

Scriptural Insight
_____
_____
_____
_____
_____
_____

Prayer
_____
_____
_____
_____
_____
_____

Application:
_____
_____

☆	my meditation for today	A	Adoration
➤	further study needed	C	Confession
x	cross reference	T	Thanksgiving
m	verse(s) to memorize	P	Petition

WEDNESDAY

Application:

THURSDAY

Application:

FRIDAY

Application:

SATURDAY

Application:

Scriptural Insights and Prayer

Scripture Memory Review	Date_____
_____	Memory Verse for the Week
_____	_____
_____	_____
_____	_____
S M T W T F S ☐ ☐ ☐ ☐ ☐ ☐ ☐	_____

	Scriptural Insight	Prayer
S U N D A Y	_____	_____
	Application:	
M O N D A Y	_____	_____
	Application:	
T U E S D A Y	_____	_____
	Application:	

☆	my meditation for today	A	Adoration
➤	further study needed	C	Confession
x	cross reference	T	Thanksgiving
m	verse(s) to memorize	P	Petition

QUIET TIME

Week 16

WEDNESDAY

Application:

THURSDAY

Application:

FRIDAY

Application:

SATURDAY

Application:

-59-

Scriptural Insights and Prayer

Scripture Memory Review	Date_____
_____	Memory Verse for the Week
_____	_____
_____	_____
_____	_____
S M T W T F S ☐ ☐ ☐ ☐ ☐ ☐ ☐	_____

	Scriptural Insight	Prayer
S U N D A Y		
	Application:	
M O N D A Y		
	Application:	
T U E S D A Y		
	Application:	

☆	my meditation for today	A	Adoration
➤	further study needed	C	Confession
x	cross reference	T	Thanksgiving
m	verse(s) to memorize	P	Petition

WEDNESDAY

Application:

THURSDAY

Application:

FRIDAY

Application:

SATURDAY

Application:

Scriptural Insights and Prayer

<table>
<tr><td>Scripture Memory Review
_____
_____
_____
_____

S M T W T F S
☐ ☐ ☐ ☐ ☐ ☐ ☐</td><td>Date_____
Memory Verse for the Week
_____
_____
_____
_____
_____</td></tr>
</table>

	Scriptural Insight	Prayer

S U N D A Y

Application:

M O N D A Y

Application:

T U E S D A Y

Application:

☆	my meditation for today	A	Adoration
➤	further study needed	C	Confession
x	cross reference	T	Thanksgiving
m	verse(s) to memorize	P	Petition

WEDNESDAY

Application:

THURSDAY

Application:

FRIDAY

Application:

SATURDAY

Application:

Scriptural Insights and Prayer

Scripture Memory Review	Date_____
_____	Memory Verse for the Week
_____	_____
_____	_____
_____	_____
S M T W T F S	_____
☐ ☐ ☐ ☐ ☐ ☐ ☐	_____

Scriptural Insight	Prayer

SUNDAY

Application:

MONDAY

Application:

TUESDAY

Application:

☆ my meditation for today	A Adoration
➤ further study needed	C Confession
x cross reference	T Thanksgiving
m verse(s) to memorize	P Petition

-64-

QUIET TIME

Week 19 ....

WEDNESDAY

Application:

THURSDAY

Application:

FRIDAY

Application:

SATURDAY

Application:

Scriptural Insights and Prayer

Scripture Memory Review	Date_____
_____	Memory Verse for the Week
_____	_____
_____	_____
_____	_____
S M T W T F S	_____
☐ ☐ ☐ ☐ ☐ ☐ ☐	_____

Scriptural Insight	Prayer

SUNDAY

Application:

MONDAY

Application:

TUESDAY

Application:

☆	my meditation for today	A	Adoration
➜	further study needed	C	Confession
x	cross reference	T	Thanksgiving
m	verse(s) to memorize	P	Petition

QUIET TIME

Week 20

WEDNESDAY

Application:

THURSDAY

Application:

FRIDAY

Application:

SATURDAY

Application:

Scriptural Insights and Prayer

Scripture Memory Review	Date_____
_____	Memory Verse for the Week
_____	_____
_____	_____
_____	_____
S M T W T F S ☐ ☐ ☐ ☐ ☐ ☐ ☐	_____

	Scriptural Insight	Prayer
S U N D A Y		
	Application:	
M O N D A Y		
	Application:	
T U E S D A Y		
	Application:	

☆	my meditation for today	A	Adoration
➤	further study needed	C	Confession
x	cross reference	T	Thanksgiving
m	verse(s) to memorize	P	Petition

QUIET TIME

Week 21

WEDNESDAY

Application:

THURSDAY

Application:

FRIDAY

Application:

SATURDAY

Application:

Scriptural Insights and Prayer

Date_____

Memory Verse for the Week
_____
_____
_____
_____
_____

Scriptural Insight	Prayer

SUNDAY

Application:

MONDAY

Application:

TUESDAY

Application:

☆	my meditation for today	A	Adoration
➤	further study needed	C	Confession
x	cross reference	T	Thanksgiving
m	verse(s) to memorize	P	Petition

QUIET TIME

Week 22

WEDNESDAY

Application:

THURSDAY

Application:

FRIDAY

Application:

SATURDAY

Application:

Scriptural Insights and Prayer

Scripture Memory Review	Date_____
_____	Memory Verse for the Week
_____	_____
_____	_____
_____	_____
S M T W T F S ☐ ☐ ☐ ☐ ☐ ☐ ☐	_____

	Scriptural Insight	Prayer
S U N D A Y	_____ _____ _____ _____ _____ _____ _____	_____ _____ _____ _____ _____ _____ _____
	Application:	
M O N D A Y	_____ _____ _____ _____ _____ _____	_____ _____ _____ _____ _____ _____
	Application:	
T U E S D A Y	_____ _____ _____ _____ _____ _____	_____ _____ _____ _____ _____ _____
	Application:	

☆ my meditation for today	A Adoration
➤ further study needed	C Confession
x cross reference	T Thanksgiving
m verse(s) to memorize	P Petition

QUIET TIME

Week 23

WEDNESDAY

Application:

THURSDAY

Application:

FRIDAY

Application:

SATURDAY

Application:

Scriptural Insights and Prayer

Scripture Memory Review	Date_____
	Memory Verse for the Week

S M T W T F S
☐ ☐ ☐ ☐ ☐ ☐ ☐

Scriptural Insight	Prayer

S U N D A Y

Application:

M O N D A Y

Application:

T U E S D A Y

Application:

☆	my meditation for today	A	Adoration
➤	further study needed	C	Confession
x	cross reference	T	Thanksgiving
m	verse(s) to memorize	P	Petition

WEDNESDAY

Application:

THURSDAY

Application:

FRIDAY

Application:

SATURDAY

Application:

Scriptural Insights and Prayer

Scripture Memory Review	Date_____
_____	Memory Verse for the Week
_____	_____
_____	_____
_____	_____
S M T W T F S ☐ ☐ ☐ ☐ ☐ ☐ ☐	_____

Scriptural Insight	Prayer

S U N D A Y

Application:

M O N D A Y

Application:

T U E S D A Y

Application:

☆	my meditation for today	A	Adoration
➤	further study needed	C	Confession
x	cross reference	T	Thanksgiving
m	verse(s) to memorize	P	Petition

WEDNESDAY

Application:

THURSDAY

Application:

FRIDAY

Application:

SATURDAY

Application:

Scriptural Insights and Prayer

Scripture Memory Review	Date_____
_____	Memory Verse for the Week
_____	_____
_____	_____
_____	_____
S M T W T F S ☐ ☐ ☐ ☐ ☐ ☐ ☐	_____

	Scriptural Insight	Prayer
S U N D A Y	_____	_____
	Application:

	Scriptural Insight	Prayer
M O N D A Y	_____	_____
	Application:

	Scriptural Insight	Prayer
T U E S D A Y	_____	_____
	Application:

☆	my meditation for today	A	Adoration
➤	further study needed	C	Confession
x	cross reference	T	Thanksgiving
m	verse(s) to memorize	P	Petition

WEDNESDAY

Application:

THURSDAY

Application:

FRIDAY

Application:

SATURDAY

Application:

Scriptural Insights and Prayer

Scripture Memory Review	Date_____
_____	Memory Verse for the Week
_____	_____
_____	_____
_____	_____
S M T W T F S	_____
☐ ☐ ☐ ☐ ☐ ☐ ☐	_____

Scriptural Insight	Prayer

S U N D A Y

Application:

M O N D A Y

Application:

T U E S D A Y

Application:

☆ my meditation for today	A Adoration
➤ further study needed	C Confession
x cross reference	T Thanksgiving
m verse(s) to memorize	P Petition

WEDNESDAY

Application:

THURSDAY

Application:

FRIDAY

Application:

SATURDAY

Application:

QUIET TIME

Week 27 ....

Scriptural Insights and Prayer

Scripture Memory Review	Date_____
_____	Memory Verse for the Week
_____	_____
_____	_____
_____	_____
S M T W T F S	_____
☐ ☐ ☐ ☐ ☐ ☐ ☐	_____

	Scriptural Insight	Prayer
S U N D A Y	_____ _____ _____ _____ _____	_____ _____ _____ _____ _____
	Application:	
M O N D A Y	_____ _____ _____ _____ _____	_____ _____ _____ _____ _____
	Application:	
T U E S D A Y	_____ _____ _____ _____ _____	_____ _____ _____ _____ _____
	Application:	

☆	my meditation for today	A	Adoration
➤	further study needed	C	Confession
x	cross reference	T	Thanksgiving
m	verse(s) to memorize	P	Petition

WEDNESDAY

Application:

THURSDAY

Application:

FRIDAY

Application:

SATURDAY

Application:

Week 28 ....

Scriptural Insights and Prayer

Scriptural Insight	Prayer

S U N D A Y

Application:

M O N D A Y

Application:

T U E S D A Y

Application:

☆ my meditation for today	A	Adoration
➜ further study needed	C	Confession
x cross reference	T	Thanksgiving
m verse(s) to memorize	P	Petition

WEDNESDAY

Application:

THURSDAY

Application:

FRIDAY

Application:

SATURDAY

Application:

Scriptural Insights and Prayer

Scripture Memory Review	Date_____
_____	Memory Verse for the Week
_____	_____
_____	_____
_____	_____
S M T W T F S	_____
☐ ☐ ☐ ☐ ☐ ☐ ☐	_____

Scriptural Insight	Prayer

SUNDAY

Application:

MONDAY

Application:

TUESDAY

Application:

☆ my meditation for today	A Adoration
➤ further study needed	C Confession
x cross reference	T Thanksgiving
m verse(s) to memorize	P Petition

WEDNESDAY

Application:

THURSDAY

Application:

FRIDAY

Application:

SATURDAY

Application:

Scriptural Insights and Prayer

Scripture Memory Review	Date_____
_____	Memory Verse for the Week
_____	_____
_____	_____
_____	_____
S M T W T F S	_____
☐ ☐ ☐ ☐ ☐ ☐ ☐	_____

	Scriptural Insight	Prayer

SUNDAY

_____   _____
_____   _____
_____   _____
_____   _____
_____   _____
_____   _____
_____   _____

Application:
_____
_____
_____

MONDAY

_____   _____
_____   _____
_____   _____
_____   _____
_____   _____
_____   _____
_____   _____

Application:
_____
_____
_____

TUESDAY

_____   _____
_____   _____
_____   _____
_____   _____
_____   _____
_____   _____
_____   _____

Application:
_____
_____
_____

☆ my meditation for today	A Adoration
➜ further study needed	C Confession
x cross reference	T Thanksgiving
m verse(s) to memorize	P Petition

QUIET TIME

Week 31

WEDNESDAY

Application:

THURSDAY

Application:

FRIDAY

Application:

SATURDAY

Application:

Scriptural Insights and Prayer

Scripture Memory Review	Date_____
_____	Memory Verse for the Week
_____	_____
_____	_____
_____	_____
S M T W T F S	_____
☐ ☐ ☐ ☐ ☐ ☐ ☐	

	Scriptural Insight	Prayer
S U N D A Y		
	Application:	
M O N D A Y		
	Application:	
T U E S D A Y		
	Application:	

☆	my meditation for today	A	Adoration
➜	further study needed	C	Confession
x	cross reference	T	Thanksgiving
m	verse(s) to memorize	P	Petition

QUIET TIME

Week 32

WEDNESDAY

Application:

THURSDAY

Application:

FRIDAY

Application:

SATURDAY

Application:

-91-

Scriptural Insights and Prayer

Scripture Memory Review	Date_____
	Memory Verse for the Week
S M T W T F S	
☐ ☐ ☐ ☐ ☐ ☐ ☐	

	Scriptural Insight	Prayer
S U N D A Y		
	Application:	
M O N D A Y		
	Application:	
T U E S D A Y		
	Application:	

☆ my meditation for today	A Adoration
➤ further study needed	C Confession
x cross reference	T Thanksgiving
m verse(s) to memorize	P Petition

WEDNESDAY

Application:

THURSDAY

Application:

FRIDAY

Application:

SATURDAY

Application:

QUIET TIME

Week 33

Scriptural Insights and Prayer

Scripture Memory Review	Date_____
_____	Memory Verse for the Week
_____	_____
_____	_____
S M T W T F S ☐ ☐ ☐ ☐ ☐ ☐ ☐	_____

Scriptural Insight	Prayer

SUNDAY

Application:

MONDAY

Application:

TUESDAY

Application:

☆	my meditation for today	A	Adoration
➤	further study needed	C	Confession
x	cross reference	T	Thanksgiving
m	verse(s) to memorize	P	Petition

WEDNESDAY

Application:

THURSDAY

Application:

FRIDAY

Application:

SATURDAY

Application:

QUIET TIME

Week 34

Scriptural Insights and Prayer

Scripture Memory Review	Date_____
_____	Memory Verse for the Week
_____	_____
_____	_____
S M T W T F S	_____
☐ ☐ ☐ ☐ ☐ ☐ ☐	_____

Scriptural Insight	Prayer

SUNDAY

Application:

MONDAY

Application:

TUESDAY

Application:

☆ my meditation for today	A Adoration
➤ further study needed	C Confession
x cross reference	T Thanksgiving
m verse(s) to memorize	P Petition

WEDNESDAY

Application:

THURSDAY

Application:

FRIDAY

Application:

SATURDAY

Application:

Scriptural Insights and Prayer

Scripture Memory Review	Date_____
_____	Memory Verse for the Week
_____	_____
_____	_____
_____	_____
S M T W T F S	_____
☐ ☐ ☐ ☐ ☐ ☐ ☐	_____

	Scriptural Insight	Prayer
S U N D A Y	_____	_____
	Application:	
M O N D A Y	_____	_____
	Application:	
T U E S D A Y	_____	_____
	Application:	

☆ my meditation for today	A Adoration
➜ further study needed	C Confession
x cross reference	T Thanksgiving
m verse(s) to memorize	P Petition

WEDNESDAY

Application:

THURSDAY

Application:

FRIDAY

Application:

SATURDAY

Application:

Scriptural Insights and Prayer

Scripture Memory Review	Date_____
_____	Memory Verse for the Week
_____	_____
_____	_____
S M T W T F S	_____
☐ ☐ ☐ ☐ ☐ ☐ ☐	_____

Scriptural Insight	Prayer

SUNDAY

Application:

MONDAY

Application:

TUESDAY

Application:

☆	my meditation for today	A	Adoration
➤	further study needed	C	Confession
x	cross reference	T	Thanksgiving
m	verse(s) to memorize	P	Petition

QUIET TIME

Week 37

WEDNESDAY

Application:

THURSDAY

Application:

FRIDAY

Application:

SATURDAY

Application:

Scriptural Insights and Prayer

Scripture Memory Review	Date_____
_____	Memory Verse for the Week
_____	_____
_____	_____
_____	_____
S M T W T F S	_____
☐ ☐ ☐ ☐ ☐ ☐ ☐	_____

	Scriptural Insight	Prayer
S U N D A Y	_____	_____
	Application:

M O N D A Y	_____	_____
	Application:

T U E S D A Y	_____	_____
	Application:

☆	my meditation for today	A	Adoration
➤	further study needed	C	Confession
x	cross reference	T	Thanksgiving
m	verse(s) to memorize	P	Petition

QUIET TIME

Week 38

WEDNESDAY

Application:

THURSDAY

Application:

FRIDAY

Application:

SATURDAY

Application:

Scriptural Insights and Prayer

Scripture Memory Review	Date_____
_____	Memory Verse for the Week
_____	_____
_____	_____
_____	_____
S M T W T F S ☐ ☐ ☐ ☐ ☐ ☐ ☐	_____
	_____

	Scriptural Insight	Prayer

S U N D A Y

Application:

M O N D A Y

Application:

T U E S D A Y

Application:

☆	my meditation for today	A	Adoration
➤	further study needed	C	Confession
x	cross reference	T	Thanksgiving
m	verse(s) to memorize	P	Petition

WEDNESDAY

Application:

THURSDAY

Application:

FRIDAY

Application:

SATURDAY

Application:

QUIET TIME

Week 39

Scriptural Insights and Prayer

Scripture Memory Review	Date_____
_____	Memory Verse for the Week
_____	_____
_____	_____
_____	_____
S M T W T F S	_____
☐ ☐ ☐ ☐ ☐ ☐ ☐	_____

	Scriptural Insight	Prayer
S U N D A Y		
	Application:	
M O N D A Y		
	Application:	
T U E S D A Y		
	Application:	

☆ my meditation for today	A Adoration
➤ further study needed	C Confession
x cross reference	T Thanksgiving
m verse(s) to memorize	P Petition

WEDNESDAY

Application:

THURSDAY

Application:

FRIDAY

Application:

SATURDAY

Application:

Scriptural Insights and Prayer

Scripture Memory Review	Date_____
_____	Memory Verse for the Week
_____	_____
_____	_____
_____	_____
S M T W T F S	_____
☐ ☐ ☐ ☐ ☐ ☐ ☐	_____

Scriptural Insight	Prayer

SUNDAY

Application:

MONDAY

Application:

TUESDAY

Application:

☆ my meditation for today	A Adoration
➤ further study needed	C Confession
x cross reference	T Thanksgiving
m verse(s) to memorize	P Petition

-108-

QUIET TIME

WEDNESDAY

Application:

THURSDAY

Application:

FRIDAY

Application:

SATURDAY

Application:

Week 41

Scriptural Insights and Prayer

Scripture Memory Review	Date_____
_____	Memory Verse for the Week
_____	_____
_____	_____
_____	_____
S M T W T F S ☐ ☐ ☐ ☐ ☐ ☐ ☐	_____

	Scriptural Insight	Prayer
S U N D A Y	_____ _____ _____ _____ _____ _____	_____ _____ _____ _____ _____ _____
	Application:	
M O N D A Y	_____ _____ _____ _____ _____ _____	_____ _____ _____ _____ _____ _____
	Application:	
T U E S D A Y	_____ _____ _____ _____ _____ _____	_____ _____ _____ _____ _____ _____
	Application:	

☆ my meditation for today	A Adoration
➤ further study needed	C Confession
x cross reference	T Thanksgiving
m verse(s) to memorize	P Petition

WEDNESDAY

Application:

THURSDAY

Application:

FRIDAY

Application:

SATURDAY

Application:

Week 42 ....

Scriptural Insights and Prayer

<table>
<tr><td>

Scripture Memory Review

_____

_____

_____

_____

S M T W T F S
☐ ☐ ☐ ☐ ☐ ☐ ☐

</td><td>

Date_____

Memory Verse for the Week

_____

_____

_____

_____

</td></tr>
</table>

Scriptural Insight	Prayer

SUNDAY

Application:

MONDAY

Application:

TUESDAY

Application:

☆	my meditation for today	A	Adoration
➤	further study needed	C	Confession
x	cross reference	T	Thanksgiving
m	verse(s) to memorize	P	Petition

WEDNESDAY

Application:

THURSDAY

Application:

FRIDAY

Application:

SATURDAY

Application:

Scriptural Insights and Prayer

Scripture Memory Review	Date_____
_____	Memory Verse for the Week
_____	_____
_____	_____
_____	_____
S M T W T F S	_____
□ □ □ □ □ □ □	_____

	Scriptural Insight	Prayer
S U N D A Y		
	Application:	
M O N D A Y		
	Application:	
T U E S D A Y		
	Application:	

☆	my meditation for today	A	Adoration
➤	further study needed	C	Confession
x	cross reference	T	Thanksgiving
m	verse(s) to memorize	P	Petition

WEDNESDAY

Application:

THURSDAY

Application:

FRIDAY

Application:

SATURDAY

Application:

QUIET TIME

Week 44 ....

Scriptural Insights and Prayer

Scripture Memory Review	Date_____
	Memory Verse for the Week

S M T W T F S
☐ ☐ ☐ ☐ ☐ ☐ ☐

Scriptural Insight	Prayer

SUNDAY

Application:

MONDAY

Application:

TUESDAY

Application:

☆   my meditation for today   A   Adoration
➤   further study needed   C   Confession
x   cross reference   T   Thanksgiving
m   verse(s) to memorize   P   Petition

WEDNESDAY

Application:

THURSDAY

Application:

FRIDAY

Application:

SATURDAY

Application:

Scriptural Insights and Prayer

Scripture Memory Review	Date_____
_____	Memory Verse for the Week
_____	_____
_____	_____
_____	_____
S M T W T F S	_____
☐ ☐ ☐ ☐ ☐ ☐ ☐	_____

Scriptural Insight	Prayer

S U N D A Y

Application:

M O N D A Y

Application:

T U E S D A Y

Application:

☆ my meditation for today	A Adoration
➤ further study needed	C Confession
x cross reference	T Thanksgiving
m verse(s) to memorize	P Petition

WEDNESDAY

Application:

THURSDAY

Application:

FRIDAY

Application:

SATURDAY

Application:

Scriptural Insights and Prayer

Scripture Memory Review	Date_____
_____	Memory Verse for the Week
_____	_____
_____	_____
_____	_____
S M T W T F S	_____
□ □ □ □ □ □ □	_____

Scriptural Insight	Prayer

SUNDAY

Application:

MONDAY

Application:

TUESDAY

Application:

☆ my meditation for today	A Adoration
➤ further study needed	C Confession
x cross reference	T Thanksgiving
m verse(s) to memorize	P Petition

WEDNESDAY

Application:

THURSDAY

Application:

FRIDAY

Application:

SATURDAY

Application:

Scriptural Insights and Prayer

Scripture Memory Review

_____
_____
_____
_____

S M T W T F S
☐ ☐ ☐ ☐ ☐ ☐ ☐

Date_____

Memory Verse for the Week

_____
_____
_____
_____
_____

Scriptural Insight	Prayer

SUNDAY

Application:

MONDAY

Application:

TUESDAY

Application:

☆ my meditation for today   A   Adoration
➤ further study needed   C   Confession
x cross reference   T   Thanksgiving
m verse(s) to memorize   P   Petition

QUIET TIME

Week 48 ....

WEDNESDAY

Application:

THURSDAY

Application:

FRIDAY

Application:

SATURDAY

Application:

Scriptural Insights and Prayer

Scripture Memory Review	Date_____
_____	Memory Verse for the Week
_____	_____
_____	_____
_____	_____
S M T W T F S ☐ ☐ ☐ ☐ ☐ ☐ ☐	_____

	Scriptural Insight	Prayer
S U N D A Y	_____ _____ _____ _____ _____ _____	_____ _____ _____ _____ _____ _____
	Application:	
M O N D A Y	_____ _____ _____ _____ _____ _____	_____ _____ _____ _____ _____ _____
	Application:	
T U E S D A Y	_____ _____ _____ _____ _____ _____	_____ _____ _____ _____ _____ _____
	Application:	

☆	my meditation for today	A	Adoration
➤	further study needed	C	Confession
x	cross reference	T	Thanksgiving
m	verse(s) to memorize	P	Petition

WEDNESDAY

Application:

THURSDAY

Application:

FRIDAY

Application:

SATURDAY

Application:

QUIET TIME

Week 49 ....

Scriptural Insights and Prayer

Scripture Memory Review	Date_____
	Memory Verse for the Week

S M T W T F S
□ □ □ □ □ □ □

Scriptural Insight	Prayer

S U N D A Y

Application:

M O N D A Y

Application:

T U E S D A Y

Application:

☆ my meditation for today   A Adoration
➤ further study needed   C Confession
x cross reference   T Thanksgiving
m verse(s) to memorize   P Petition

WEDNESDAY

Application:

THURSDAY

Application:

FRIDAY

Application:

SATURDAY

Application:

QUIET TIME

Week 50

Scriptural Insights and Prayer

Scripture Memory Review	Date_____
_____	Memory Verse for the Week
_____	_____
_____	_____
_____	_____
S M T W T F S ☐ ☐ ☐ ☐ ☐ ☐ ☐	_____

	Scriptural Insight	Prayer
S U N D A Y	_____ _____ _____ _____ _____	_____ _____ _____ _____ _____
	Application: 	
M O N D A Y	_____ _____ _____ _____ _____	_____ _____ _____ _____ _____
	Application: 	
T U E S D A Y	_____ _____ _____ _____ _____	_____ _____ _____ _____ _____
	Application: 	

☆	my meditation for today	A	Adoration
➤	further study needed	C	Confession
x	cross reference	T	Thanksgiving
m	verse(s) to memorize	P	Petition

WEDNESDAY

Application:

THURSDAY

Application:

FRIDAY

Application:

SATURDAY

Application:

QUIET TIME

Week 51 ....

Scriptural Insights and Prayer

Scripture Memory Review
_____
_____
_____
_____

S M T W T F S
☐ ☐ ☐ ☐ ☐ ☐ ☐

Date_____

Memory Verse for the Week
_____
_____
_____
_____

Scriptural Insight	Prayer

S U N D A Y

Application:

M O N D A Y

Application:

T U E S D A Y

Application:

☆ my meditation for today	A Adoration
➤ further study needed	C Confession
x cross reference	T Thanksgiving
m verse(s) to memorize	P Petition

QUIET TIME

Week 52 ....

WEDNESDAY

Application:

THURSDAY

Application:

FRIDAY

Application:

SATURDAY

Application:

Note Taking
Section 2

NOTE TAKING

HOW TO USE THE NOTE TAKING SECTION

THIS SECTION CAN BE USED DURING:

Worship Services	**Group Bible Studies**
Evangelistic Meetings	**Conferences**

The **Journal's** approach to note taking is simplified through the use of symbols. When God impresses you with a thought during any part of a sermon, just write it down, code it, and continue note taking. After several weeks, you will become familiar with the symbols. At the end of each message, it will be easy to refer back to the subject areas which have been coded.

Explanation of Symbols:

☆ *Point to Remember:* This could be an outstanding quotation, a profound statement, or a new insight from God's Word.

➤ *Further Study Needed:* When you find a passage or thought of particular interest which you would like to study in more detail, code it with an "➤". If the word or passage is unclear, use the same code.

√ *Illustration:* Summarize good illustrations so you can remember them. You will find that the illustrations God uses to convict or challenge you will often communicate to others as well.

✕ *Cross Reference:* Many times a speaker will refer to related verses in the Bible. In each case, use an "✕" to code those references. As you become increasingly acquainted with the Scriptures, God will begin bringing references to your mind as you listen to His Word.

○ *Application:* Applying God's Word is the most important principle in living the Christian life. To *emphasize* areas for application, code your notes with a circle, "○". Notice in the example how the application portions of the notes are circled, as well as coded. You will usually find it necessary to write out *specific steps* to put your application into immediate practice. Your applications need to be:

PERSONAL: Select an activity *you* can do!
SPECIFIC: Be *detailed* and *realistic*!
MEASURABLE: Give yourself a *time limit*!

"Discipline yourself for the purpose of godliness" (1 Timothy 4:7b, NAS).

CODE		Jan. 16		☑ Sermon
☆	point to remember	date		☐ Bible Study
√	illustration	Rev. T. Jones	1 John 5:11-12	☐ Book
×	cross reference	speaker	text	☐ Cassette Tape
➤	further study needed	Knowing God		☐ Other Meeting
○	personal application	subject title		

". . . God has given us eternal life, and this life is in His Son" – v. 11

☆ To receive Christ is to begin an eternal relationship with God.

➤ "He who has the Son has life. He who does not have the Son of
God does not have life." – v. 12.

○ Lord, I thank you for the eternal life that you have given me.

☆ All men are either saved or lost. There is no middle ground!

√ Salvation resembles marriage. If I ask, "Are you married?" you
would not answer, "I hope so", or "Perhaps". Only one of two
answers could be correct: "Yes" or "No". The same is true with
salvation. Either we have invited Jesus Christ into our hearts as
Saviour, or we have not.

m Jesus said, "I am the way, the truth, and the life. No man comes unto the
x Father but by Me" (John 14:6). Christ is the only way to heaven!

The message of Christianity is unique. Jesus did not claim to be one
prophet among many. He claimed to be the only Saviour. Because of His
death on the cross on our behalf, we can choose to know God as our
Father, rather than our judge.

☆ Every year millions of people die with no knowledge of Jesus Christ.

○ I need to develop a deeper burden for non-Christians.

○ This week I will talk to John Smith about what it means to be a Christian.

". . . Faith cometh by hearing . . ."

NOTE TAKING

INDEX TO SERMONS AND TALKS

SUBJECT	TEXT	SPEAKER	PAGE NO

INDEX TO SERMONS AND TALKS

SUBJECT	TEXT	SPEAKER	PAGE NO

NOTE TAKING

CODE
☆ point to remember
∨ illustration
✕ cross reference
➤ further study needed
○ personal application

_____ date _____

☐ Sermon
☐ Bible Study
☐ Book
☐ Cassette Tape
☐ Other Meeting

speaker _____ text

_____ subject title _____

2 Chronicles 16:9 - for the eyes of the
Lord run to & fro throughout the
whole earth to show Himself
strong in behalf of those whose
hearts are blameless towards
Him

_____ date _____ ☐ Sermon
                                        ☐ Bible Study
speaker _____ text ☐ Book
                                        ☐ Cassette Tape
_____ ☐ Other Meeting
            subject title

NOTE TAKING

"... *Faith cometh by hearing* ..."

_____ date _____ ☐ Sermon

☐ Bible Study

speaker _____ text _____ ☐ Book

☐ Cassette Tape

_____ subject title _____ ☐ Other Meeting

". . . Faith cometh by hearing . . ."

_____ date
☐ Sermon
☐ Bible Study
speaker _____ text _____ ☐ Book
☐ Cassette Tape
_____ subject title _____ ☐ Other Meeting

NOTE TAKING

". . . Faith cometh by hearing . . ."

date _____

speaker _____   text _____

subject title _____

☐ Sermon
☐ Bible Study
☐ Book
☐ Cassette Tape
☐ Other Meeting

". . . Faith cometh by hearing . . ."

_____ date ☐ Sermon
                    ☐ Bible Study
_____ _____ ☐ Book
speaker   text ☐ Cassette Tape
_____ ☐ Other Meeting
       subject title

NOTE TAKING

". . . Faith cometh by hearing . . ."

_____
date   ☐ Sermon
                        ☐ Bible Study
speaker   text   ☐ Book
                        ☐ Cassette Tape
_____   ☐ Other Meeting
subject title

_____
_____
_____
_____
_____
_____
_____
_____
_____
_____
_____
_____
_____
_____
_____
_____
_____
_____
_____
_____
_____
_____
_____
_____
_____
_____
_____
_____
_____
_____
_____
_____

". . . Faith cometh by hearing . . ."

CODE
☆ point to remember
∨ illustration
✕ cross reference
➤ further study needed
○ personal application

_____ date _____ ☐ Sermon
                              ☐ Bible Study
speaker _____ text ___ ☐ Book
                              ☐ Cassette Tape
_____ subject title ___ ☐ Other Meeting

NOTE TAKING

". . . Faith cometh by hearing . . ."

CODE
☆ point to remember
∨ illustration
✕ cross reference
➤ further study needed
○ personal application

_____
date

□ Sermon
□ Bible Study
□ Book
□ Cassette Tape
□ Other Meeting

speaker _____ _____ text

_____
subject title

" . . . *Faith cometh by hearing* . . ."

CODE
☆ point to remember
∨ illustration
✕ cross reference
➤ further study needed
○ personal application

_____
date

☐ Sermon
☐ Bible Study

speaker _____ text ☐ Book

☐ Cassette Tape

_____
subject title

☐ Other Meeting

NOTE TAKING

". . . Faith cometh by hearing . . ."

-147-

_____
date

☐ Sermon
☐ Bible Study
☐ Book
☐ Cassette Tape
☐ Other Meeting

speaker _____ text

_____
subject title

". . . Faith cometh by hearing . . ."

CODE
☆ point to remember
∨ illustration
✕ cross reference
➤ further study needed
○ personal application

_____ date _____   ☐ Sermon
                              ☐ Bible Study
speaker _____ _____ text ☐ Book
                              ☐ Cassette Tape
_____ subject title _____ ☐ Other Meeting

NOTE TAKING

". . . Faith cometh by hearing . . ."

-149-

CODE
☆ point to remember
∨ illustration
× cross reference
➤ further study needed
○ personal application

_____ date _____ ☐ Sermon
☐ Bible Study
speaker _____ text ☐ Book
☐ Cassette Tape
_____ subject title _____ ☐ Other Meeting

". . . Faith cometh by hearing . . ."

_____ date _____   ☐ Sermon
                                        ☐ Bible Study
speaker _____ text   ☐ Book
                                        ☐ Cassette Tape
_____ subject title   ☐ Other Meeting

NOTE TAKING

_____
_____
_____
_____
_____
_____
_____
_____
_____
_____
_____
_____
_____
_____
_____
_____
_____
_____
_____
_____
_____
_____
_____
_____
_____
_____
_____
_____
_____
_____
_____
_____
_____
_____
_____
_____

". . . Faith cometh by hearing . . ."

CODE		
☆ point to remember	date	☐ Sermon
V illustration		☐ Bible Study
× cross reference	speaker text	☐ Book
➤ further study needed		☐ Cassette Tape
○ personal application	subject title	☐ Other Meeting

". . . Faith cometh by hearing . . ."

CODE
☆ point to remember
∨ illustration
✕ cross reference
➤ further study needed
○ personal application

_____ date
_____

speaker _____ text

_____ subject title

☐ Sermon
☐ Bible Study
☐ Book
☐ Cassette Tape
☐ Other Meeting

NOTE TAKING

_____
_____
_____
_____
_____
_____
_____
_____
_____
_____
_____
_____
_____
_____
_____
_____
_____
_____
_____
_____
_____
_____
_____
_____
_____
_____
_____
_____
_____
_____
_____
_____
_____
_____
_____
_____
_____

". . . Faith cometh by hearing . . ."

_____ date _____ ☐ Sermon
                               ☐ Bible Study
speaker _____ text _____ ☐ Book
                               ☐ Cassette Tape
_____ subject title ___ ☐ Other Meeting

"... Faith cometh by hearing ..."

_____ date _____   ☐ Sermon
                                               ☐ Bible Study
_____   _____ text   ☐ Book
speaker   ☐ Cassette Tape
_____   ☐ Other Meeting
                subject title

NOTE TAKING

". . . Faith cometh by hearing . . ."

_____ date _____ □ Sermon
                                        □ Bible Study
speaker _____ text   □ Book
                                        □ Cassette Tape
_____ subject title _____ □ Other Meeting

_____

_____

_____

_____

_____

_____

_____

_____

_____

_____

_____

_____

_____

_____

_____

_____

_____

_____

_____

_____

_____

_____

_____

_____

_____

_____

_____

_____

_____

_____

_____

_____

_____

_____

_____

_____

_____

_____

_____

_____

_____

_____

_____

". . . Faith cometh by hearing . . ."

CODE
☆ point to remember
∨ illustration
✕ cross reference
➤ further study needed
○ personal application

_____ date _____   ☐ Sermon
                                    ☐ Bible Study
speaker _____ text _____ ☐ Book
                                    ☐ Cassette Tape
_____ subject title _____ ☐ Other Meeting

NOTE TAKING

". . . Faith cometh by hearing . . ."

-157-

_____
date

speaker _____   text _____

_____
subject title

☐ Sermon
☐ Bible Study
☐ Book
☐ Cassette Tape
☐ Other Meeting

". . . Faith cometh by hearing . . ."

_____
date   □ Sermon
                        □ Bible Study
speaker _____ text □ Book
                        □ Cassette Tape
_____   □ Other Meeting
subject title

NOTE TAKING

". . . Faith cometh by hearing . . ."

_____
date

☐ Sermon
☐ Bible Study
☐ Book
☐ Cassette Tape
☐ Other Meeting

speaker   text

_____
subject title

_____
_____
_____
_____
_____
_____
_____
_____
_____
_____
_____
_____
_____
_____
_____
_____
_____
_____
_____
_____
_____
_____
_____
_____
_____
_____
_____
_____
_____
_____
_____
_____
_____
_____
_____
_____
_____
_____
_____
_____

". . . Faith cometh by hearing . . ."

_____
date

speaker   text

_____
subject title

☐ Sermon
☐ Bible Study
☐ Book
☐ Cassette Tape
☐ Other Meeting

NOTE TAKING

"... Faith cometh by hearing ..."

_____ date   ☐ Sermon
                                                 ☐ Bible Study
speaker   text   ☐ Book
                                                 ☐ Cassette Tape
_____   ☐ Other Meeting
                subject title

_____

_____

_____

_____

_____

_____

_____

_____

_____

_____

_____

_____

_____

_____

_____

_____

_____

_____

_____

_____

_____

_____

_____

_____

_____

_____

_____

_____

_____

_____

_____

_____

_____

_____

_____

". . . Faith cometh by hearing . . ."

CODE

☆ point to remember
∨ illustration
✕ cross reference
➤ further study needed
○ personal application

_____ date _____ ☐ Sermon
                        ☐ Bible Study
_____   _____   ☐ Book
speaker   text   ☐ Cassette Tape
_____ ☐ Other Meeting
        subject title

NOTE TAKING

_____
_____
_____
_____
_____
_____
_____
_____
_____
_____
_____
_____
_____
_____
_____
_____
_____
_____
_____
_____
_____
_____
_____
_____
_____
_____
_____
_____
_____
_____
_____
_____
_____
_____
_____
_____
_____

". . . Faith cometh by hearing . . ."

date _____

☐ Sermon
☐ Bible Study
☐ Book
☐ Cassette Tape
☐ Other Meeting

speaker _____ text _____

subject title _____

_____
_____
_____
_____
_____
_____
_____
_____
_____
_____
_____
_____
_____
_____
_____
_____
_____
_____
_____
_____
_____
_____
_____
_____
_____
_____
_____
_____
_____
_____
_____
_____
_____
_____
_____
_____
_____

". . . Faith cometh by hearing . . ."

_____ date _____   ☐ Sermon
                                     ☐ Bible Study
speaker _____ text _____ ☐ Book
                                     ☐ Cassette Tape
_____ subject title _____ ☐ Other Meeting

NOTE TAKING

_____
_____
_____
_____
_____
_____
_____
_____
_____
_____
_____
_____
_____
_____
_____
_____
_____
_____
_____
_____
_____
_____
_____
_____
_____
_____
_____
_____
_____
_____
_____
_____
_____
_____
_____

". . . Faith cometh by hearing . . ."

_____ date _____

☐ Sermon
☐ Bible Study
speaker _____ text ☐ Book
☐ Cassette Tape
_____ subject title _____ ☐ Other Meeting

"... Faith cometh by hearing ..."

_____ date

☐ Sermon
☐ Bible Study

speaker _____ text ☐ Book
☐ Cassette Tape
_____ ☐ Other Meeting
subject title

NOTE TAKING

". . . Faith cometh by hearing . . ."

CODE

☆ point to remember
∨ illustration
✕ cross reference
➤ further study needed
○ personal application

_____ date _____

speaker _____ text _____

_____
subject title

☐ Sermon
☐ Bible Study
☐ Book
☐ Cassette Tape
☐ Other Meeting

". . . Faith cometh by hearing . . ."

-168-

CODE

☆ point to remember
∨ illustration
× cross reference
➤ further study needed
○ personal application

_____
date   ☐ Sermon
                        ☐ Bible Study
_____
speaker   text   ☐ Book
                        ☐ Cassette Tape
_____
subject title   ☐ Other Meeting

NOTE TAKING

". . . Faith cometh by hearing . . ."

CODE
☆ point to remember
∨ illustration
✕ cross reference
➤ further study needed
○ personal application

_____ date _____   ☐ Sermon
                                ☐ Bible Study
speaker _____ text   ☐ Book
                                ☐ Cassette Tape
_____ subject title _____ ☐ Other Meeting

". . . Faith cometh by hearing . . ."

-170-

CODE
☆ point to remember
∨ illustration
✕ cross reference
➤ further study needed
○ personal application

_____ date   ☐ Sermon
                                  ☐ Bible Study
speaker _____ text   ☐ Book
                                  ☐ Cassette Tape
_____   ☐ Other Meeting
          subject title

NOTE TAKING

"... Faith cometh by hearing ..."

date _____ ☐ Sermon

☐ Bible Study

speaker _____ text _____ ☐ Book

☐ Cassette Tape

_____ ☐ Other Meeting
subject title

". . . Faith cometh by hearing . . ."

CODE
- ☆ point to remember
- ∨ illustration
- ✕ cross reference
- ➤ further study needed
- ○ personal application

_____
date

speaker _____ text _____

_____
subject title

- ☐ Sermon
- ☐ Bible Study
- ☐ Book
- ☐ Cassette Tape
- ☐ Other Meeting

NOTE TAKING

". . . Faith cometh by hearing . . ."

-173-

CODE
☆ point to remember
∨ illustration
✕ cross reference
➤ further study needed
○ personal application

_____ date _____ ☐ Sermon
☐ Bible Study
_____ speaker _____ text ☐ Book
☐ Cassette Tape
_____ subject title _____ ☐ Other Meeting

"_. . . Faith cometh by hearing . . ._"

_____ date

☐ Sermon
☐ Bible Study

speaker _____ _____ text ☐ Book
☐ Cassette Tape
_____ subject title ☐ Other Meeting

NOTE TAKING

_____
_____
_____
_____
_____
_____
_____
_____
_____
_____
_____
_____
_____
_____
_____
_____
_____
_____
_____
_____
_____
_____
_____
_____
_____
_____
_____
_____
_____
_____
_____

". . . Faith cometh by hearing . . ."

CODE
☆ point to remember
∨ illustration
× cross reference
➤ further study needed
○ personal application

_____
date
_____
speaker

_____
text

_____
subject title

☐ Sermon
☐ Bible Study
☐ Book
☐ Cassette Tape
☐ Other Meeting

_____
_____
_____
_____
_____
_____
_____
_____
_____
_____
_____
_____
_____
_____
_____
_____
_____
_____
_____
_____
_____
_____
_____
_____
_____
_____
_____
_____
_____
_____
_____
_____
_____
_____
_____
_____
_____
_____

". . . Faith cometh by hearing . . ."

date _____

☐ Sermon
☐ Bible Study

speaker _____ _____ text ☐ Book
☐ Cassette Tape

subject title _____ ☐ Other Meeting

NOTE TAKING

"_. . . Faith cometh by hearing . . ._"

CODE
☆ point to remember
∨ illustration
× cross reference
➤ further study needed
○ personal application

_____ date _____   ☐ Sermon
                                ☐ Bible Study
_____ speaker _____ text ☐ Book
                                ☐ Cassette Tape
_____ ☐ Other Meeting
              subject title

". . . Faith cometh by hearing . . ."

CODE
☆ point to remember
∨ illustration
× cross reference
➤ further study needed
○ personal application

_____
date   ☐ Sermon
                        ☐ Bible Study
speaker   text   ☐ Book
                        ☐ Cassette Tape
_____   ☐ Other Meeting
subject title

NOTE TAKING

". . . Faith cometh by hearing . . ."

CODE
☆ point to remember
∨ illustration
✕ cross reference
➜ further study needed
○ personal application

_____ date

_____ _____
speaker   text

_____
subject title

☐ Sermon
☐ Bible Study
☐ Book
☐ Cassette Tape
☐ Other Meeting

". . . Faith cometh by hearing . . ."

CODE
☆ point to remember
∨ illustration
✕ cross reference
➤ further study needed
○ personal application

_____
date

☐ Sermon
☐ Bible Study
☐ Book
☐ Cassette Tape
☐ Other Meeting

_____ _____
speaker   text

_____
subject title

NOTE TAKING

". . . Faith cometh by hearing . . ."

_____ date _____   □ Sermon
                                                □ Bible Study
_____   _____   □ Book
speaker   text   □ Cassette Tape
                                                □ Other Meeting
_____
                subject title

_____
_____
_____
_____
_____
_____
_____
_____
_____
_____
_____
_____
_____
_____
_____
_____
_____
_____
_____
_____
_____
_____
_____
_____
_____
_____
_____
_____
_____
_____
_____
_____
_____
_____
_____
_____
_____
_____
_____
_____
_____
_____

". . . Faith cometh by hearing . . ."

CODE
☆ point to remember
∨ illustration
× cross reference
➤ further study needed
○ personal application

_____
date

speaker   text

subject title

☐ Sermon
☐ Bible Study
☐ Book
☐ Cassette Tape
☐ Other Meeting

NOTE TAKING

"... Faith cometh by hearing ..."

CODE
☆ point to remember
∨ illustration
✕ cross reference
➤ further study needed
○ personal application

_____
date

☐ Sermon
☐ Bible Study

_____ _____
speaker   text

☐ Book
☐ Cassette Tape

_____
subject title

☐ Other Meeting

". . . Faith cometh by hearing . . ."

_____
date

☐ Sermon
☐ Bible Study
_____ _____ ☐ Book
speaker   text
☐ Cassette Tape
_____ ☐ Other Meeting
subject title

NOTE TAKING

"... Faith cometh by hearing ..."

_____ date _____

☐ Sermon
☐ Bible Study

speaker _____ text

☐ Book
☐ Cassette Tape

_____ subject title _____ ☐ Other Meeting

". . . Faith cometh by hearing . . ."

CODE

☆ point to remember
∨ illustration
✕ cross reference
➤ further study needed
○ personal application

_____
date   ☐ Sermon
                        ☐ Bible Study
_____ _____ ☐ Book
speaker   text   ☐ Cassette Tape
                        ☐ Other Meeting
_____
subject title

NOTE TAKING

_____

_____

_____

_____

_____

_____

_____

_____

_____

_____

_____

_____

_____

_____

_____

_____

_____

_____

_____

_____

_____

_____

_____

_____

_____

_____

_____

_____

_____

_____

_____

_____

_____

". . . Faith cometh by hearing . . ."

CODE
☆ point to remember
V illustration
× cross reference
➤ further study needed
○ personal application

_____ date _____ ☐ Sermon
                               ☐ Bible Study
speaker _____ text ___ ☐ Book
                               ☐ Cassette Tape
_____ subject title ___ ☐ Other Meeting

". . . Faith cometh by hearing . . ."

CODE		
☆ point to remember	_____ date _____	☐ Sermon
∨ illustration		☐ Bible Study
✕ cross reference	speaker _____ _____ text	☐ Book
➤ further study needed		☐ Cassette Tape
○ personal application	_____ subject title _____	☐ Other Meeting

NOTE TAKING

". . . Faith cometh by hearing . . ."

_____ date _____

□ Sermon
□ Bible Study

_____ speaker _____ text

□ Book
□ Cassette Tape

_____ subject title _____

□ Other Meeting

_____
_____
_____
_____
_____
_____
_____
_____
_____
_____
_____
_____
_____
_____
_____
_____
_____
_____
_____
_____
_____
_____
_____
_____
_____
_____
_____
_____
_____
_____
_____
_____
_____
_____
_____
_____
_____
_____
_____
_____
_____
_____
_____
_____

". . . Faith cometh by hearing . . ."

_____ date
☐ Sermon
☐ Bible Study
_____ speaker _____ text ☐ Book
☐ Cassette Tape
_____ subject title ☐ Other Meeting

NOTE TAKING

". . . Faith cometh by hearing . . ."

_____
date   ☐ Sermon
                            ☐ Bible Study
speaker   text   ☐ Book
                            ☐ Cassette Tape
_____   ☐ Other Meeting
subject title

". . . Faith cometh by hearing . . ."

_____ date _____   ☐ Sermon
                            ☐ Bible Study
speaker _____ text _____ ☐ Book
                            ☐ Cassette Tape
_____ ☐ Other Meeting
          subject title

NOTE TAKING

". . . Faith cometh by hearing . . ."

CODE
☆ point to remember
∨ illustration
✕ cross reference
➤ further study needed
○ personal application

_____ date _____ ☐ Sermon
                                ☐ Bible Study
speaker _____ text ____ ☐ Book
                                ☐ Cassette Tape
_____ subject title ____ ☐ Other Meeting

"... Faith cometh by hearing ..."

_____
date

□ Sermon
□ Bible Study
□ Book
□ Cassette Tape
□ Other Meeting

_____   _____
speaker   text

_____
subject title

NOTE TAKING

". . . Faith cometh by hearing . . ."

_____ date
speaker _____ text
_____ subject title

☐ Sermon
☐ Bible Study
☐ Book
☐ Cassette Tape
☐ Other Meeting

". . . Faith cometh by hearing . . ."

CODE
☆ point to remember
∨ illustration
× cross reference
➤ further study needed
○ personal application

_____ date _____   ☐ Sermon
                          ☐ Bible Study
speaker _____ text ____ ☐ Book
                          ☐ Cassette Tape
_____ subject title ____ ☐ Other Meeting

NOTE TAKING

". . . Faith cometh by hearing . . ."

CODE
☆ point to remember
∨ illustration
✕ cross reference
➤ further study needed
○ personal application

_____ date

☐ Sermon
☐ Bible Study
speaker _____ text ☐ Book
☐ Cassette Tape
_____ subject title _____ ☐ Other Meeting

". . . Faith cometh by hearing . . ."

CODE

☆ point to remember
∨ illustration
✕ cross reference
➤ further study needed
○ personal application

_____
date

☐ Sermon
☐ Bible Study

speaker   text   ☐ Book
                                  ☐ Cassette Tape
_____
subject title   ☐ Other Meeting

NOTE TAKING

". . . Faith cometh by hearing . . ."

Additional Aids
Section 3

BIBLE READING PLAN

To use the Quiet Time portion of your devotional guide effectively, it is necessary to have a plan for consistent daily Bible reading. Plan to read at a pace that is comfortable for you. Strive for understanding and not just quantity.

If you decide to read the Bible through in a year, you may choose to read from the Old Testament in the mornings and from the New Testament in the evenings.

If you prefer reading at a slower pace, try reading only the New Testament passage each morning. This will require only *20 to 25 verses* per day!

JANUARY

DATE	MORNING		EVENING	
1	GEN.	1,2	MATT.	1
2	GEN.	3,4,5	MATT.	2
3	GEN.	6,7,8	MATT.	3
4	GEN.	9,10,11	MATT.	4
5	GEN.	12,13,14	MATT.	5:1-26
6	GEN.	15,16,17	MATT.	5:27-48
7	GEN.	18,19	MATT.	6
8	GEN.	20,21,22	MATT.	7
9	GEN.	23,24	MATT.	8
10	GEN.	25,26	MATT.	9:1-17
11	GEN.	27,28	MATT.	9:18-38
12	GEN.	29,30	MATT.	10:1-23
13	GEN.	31,32	MATT.	10:24-42
14	GEN.	33,34,35	MATT.	11
15	GEN.	36,37	MATT.	12:1-21
16	GEN.	38,39,40	MATT.	12:22-50
17	GEN.	41	MATT.	13:1-32
18	GEN.	42,43	MATT.	13:33-58
19	GEN.	44,45	MATT.	14:1-21
20	GEN.	46,47,48	MATT.	14:22-36
21	GEN.	49-50	MATT.	15:1-20
22	EXOD.	1,2,3	MATT.	15:21-39
23	EXOD.	4,5,6	MATT.	16
24	EXOD.	7,8	MATT.	17
25	EXOD.	9,10	MATT.	18:1-20
26	EXOD.	11,12	MATT.	18:21.35
27	EXOD.	13,14,15	MATT.	19:1-15
28	EXOD.	16,17,18	MATT.	19:16-30
29	EXOD.	19,20,21	MATT.	20:1-16
30	EXOD.	22,23,24	MATT.	20:17-34
31	EXOD.	25,26	MATT.	21:1-22

FEBRUARY

DATE	MORNING		EVENING	
1	EXOD.	27,28	MATT.	21:23-46
2	EXOD.	29,30	MATT.	22:1-22
3	EXOD.	31,32,33	MATT.	22:23-46
4	EXOD.	34,35,36	MATT.	23:1-22
5	EXOD.	37,38	MATT.	23:23-39
6	EXOD.	39,40	MATT.	24:1-22
7	LEV.	1,2,3	MATT.	24:23-51
8	LEV.	4,5,6	MATT.	25:1-30
9	LEV.	7,8,9	MATT.	25:31-46
10	LEV.	10,11,12	MATT.	26:1-19
11	LEV.	13	MATT.	26:20-54
12	LEV.	14	MATT.	26:55-75
13	LEV.	15,16,17	MATT.	27:1-31
14	LEV.	18,19	MATT.	27:32-66
15	LEV.	20,21	MATT.	28:1-20
16	LEV.	22,23	MARK.	1:1-22
17	LEV.	24,25	MARK.	1:23-45
18	LEV.	26,27	MARK.	2
19	NUM.	1,2	MARK.	2:1-21
20	NUM.	3,4	MARK.	3:22-35
21	NUM.	5,6	MARK.	4:1-20
22	NUM.	7	MARK.	4:21-41
23	NUM.	8,9,10	MARK.	5:1-20
24	NUM.	11,12,13	MARK.	5:21-43
25	NUM.	14,15	MARK.	6:1-32
26	NUM.	16,17	MARK.	6:33-56
27	NUM.	18,19,20	MARK.	7:1-13
28	NUM.	21,22	MARK.	7:14-37
29	NUM.	23,24,25	MARK.	8:1-21

Divide chapters for Feb 29 and
read them Feb 28 and Mar 1
when Feb has only 28 days

MARCH

DATE	MORNING		EVENING	
1	NUM.	26,27	MARK.	8:22-38
2	NUM.	28,29	MARK.	9:1-29
3	NUM.	30,31	MARK.	9:30-50
4	NUM.	32,33	MARK.	10:1-31
5	NUM.	34,35,36	MARK.	10:32-50
6	DEUT.	1,2	MARK.	11:1-19
7	DEUT.	3,4	MARK.	11:20-33
8	DEUT.	5,6,7	MARK.	12:1-27
9	DEUT.	8,9,10	MARK.	12:28-44
10	DEUT.	11,12,13	MARK.	13:1-13
11	DEUT.	14,15,16	MARK.	13:14-37
12	DEUT.	17,18,19	MARK.	14:1-25
13	DEUT.	20,21,22	MARK.	14:26-50
14	DEUT.	23,24,25	MARK.	14:51-72
15	DEUT.	26,27	MARK.	15:1-26
16	DEUT.	28	MARK.	15:27-47
17	DEUT.	29,30	MARK.	16
18	DEUT.	31,32	LUKE.	1:1-23
19	DEUT.	33,34	LUKE.	1:24-56
20	JOSH.	1,2,3	LUKE.	1:57-80
21	JOSH.	4,5,6	LUKE.	2:1-24
22	JOSH.	7,8	LUKE.	2:25-52
23	JOSH.	9,10	LUKE.	3
24	JOSH.	11,12,13	LUKE.	4:1-32
25	JOSH.	14,15	LUKE.	4:33-44
26	JOSH.	16,17,18	LUKE.	5:1-16
27	JOSH.	19,20	LUKE.	5:17-39
28	JOSH.	21,22	LUKE.	6:1-26
29	JOSH.	23,24	LUKE.	6:27-49
30	JUDG.	1,2	LUKE.	7:1-30
31	JUDG.	6,7	LUKE.	7:31-50

APRIL

DATE	MORNING		EVENING	
1	JUDG.	6,7	LUKE.	8:1-21
2	JUDG.	8,9	LUKE.	8:22-56
3	JUDG.	10,11	LUKE.	9:1-36
4	JUDG.	12,13,14	LUKE.	9:37-62
5	JUDG.	15,16,17	LUKE.	10:1-24
6	JUDG.	18,19	LUKE.	10:25-42
7	JUDG.	20,21	LUKE.	11:1-28
8	RUTH.		LUKE.	11:29-54
9	I SAM.	1,2,3	LUKE.	12:1-34
10	I SAM.	4,5,6	LUKE.	12:35-59
11	I SAM.	7,8,9	LUKE.	13:1-21
12	I SAM.	10,11,12	LUKE.	13:22-35
13	I SAM.	13,14	LUKE.	14:1-24
14	I SAM.	15,16	LUKE.	14:25-35
15	I SAM.	17,18	LUKE.	15:1-10
16	I SAM.	19,20,21	LUKE.	15:11-32
17	I SAM.	22,23,24	LUKE.	16:1-18
18	I SAM.	25,26	LUKE.	16:19-31
19	I SAM.	27,28,29	LUKE.	17:1-19
20	I SAM.	30,31	LUKE.	17:20-37
21	II SAM.	1,2,3	LUKE.	18:1-17
22	II SAM.	4,5,6	LUKE.	18:18-43
23	II SAM.	7,8,9	LUKE.	19:1-28
24	II SAM.	10,11,12	LUKE.	19:29-48
25	II SAM.	13,14	LUKE.	20:1-26
26	II SAM.	15,16	LUKE.	20:27-47
27	II SAM.	17,18	LUKE.	21:1-19
28	II SAM.	19,20	LUKE.	21:20-38
29	II SAM.	21,22	LUKE.	22:1-30
30	II SAM.	23,24	LUKE.	22:31-53

MAY

DATE	MORNING		EVENING	
1	I KINGS.	1,2	LUKE.	22:54-71
2	I KINGS.	3,4,5	LUKE.	23:1-26
3	I KINGS.	6,7	LUKE.	23:27-38
4	I KINGS.	8,9	LUKE.	23:39-56
5	I KINGS.	10,11	LUKE.	24:1-35
6	I KINGS.	12,13	LUKE.	24:36-53
7	I KINGS.	14,15	JOHN.	1:1-28
8	I KINGS.	16,17,18	JOHN.	1:29-51
9	I KINGS.	19,20	JOHN.	2
10	I KINGS.	21,22	JOHN.	3:1-21
11	II KINGS.	1,2,3	JOHN.	3:22-36
12	II KINGS.	4,5	JOHN.	4:1-30
13	II KINGS.	6,7,8	JOHN.	4:31-54
14	II KINGS.	9,10,11	JOHN.	5:1-24
15	II KINGS.	12,13,14	JOHN.	5:25-47
16	II KINGS.	15,16,17	JOHN.	6:1-21
17	II KINGS.	18,19	JOHN.	6:22-44
18	II KINGS.	20,21,22	JOHN.	6:45-71
19	II KINGS.	23,24,25	JOHN.	7:1-31
20	I CHRO.	1,2	JOHN.	7:32-53
21	I CHRO.	3,4,5	JOHN.	8:1-20
22	I CHRO.	6,7	JOHN.	8:21-36
23	I CHRO.	8,9,10	JOHN.	8:37-59
24	I CHRO.	11,12,13	JOHN.	9:1-23
25	I CHRO.	14,15,16	JOHN.	9:24-41
26	I CHRO.	17,18,19	JOHN.	10:1-21
27	I CHRO.	20,21,22	JOHN.	10:22-42
28	I CHRO.	23,24,25	JOHN.	11:1-17
29	I CHRO.	26,27	JOHN.	11:18-46
30	I CHRO.	28,29	JOHN.	11:47-57
31	II CHRO.	1,2,3	JOHN.	12:1-19

JUNE

DATE	MORNING		EVENING	
1	II CHRO.	4,5,6	JOHN.	12:20-50
2	II CHRO.	7,8,9	JOHN.	13:1-17
3	II CHRO.	10,11,12	JOHN.	13:18-38
4	II CHRO.	13-16	JOHN.	14
5	II CHRO.	17,18,19	JOHN.	15
6	II CHRO.	20,21,22	JOHN.	16:1-15
7	II CHRO.	23,24,25	JOHN.	16:16-33
8	II CHRO.	26,27,28	JOHN.	17
9	II CHRO.	29,30,31	JOHN.	18:1-23
10	II CHRO.	32,33	JOHN.	18:24-40
11	II CHRO.	34,35,36	JOHN.	19:1-22
12	EZRA.	1,2	JOHN.	19:23-42
13	EZRA.	3,4,5	JOHN.	20
14	EZRA.	6,7,8	JOHN.	21
15	EZRA.	9,10	ACTS.	1
16	NEH.	1,2,3	ACTS.	2:1-13
17	NEH.	4,5,6	ACTS.	2:14-47
18	NEH.	7,8	ACTS.	3
19	NEH.	9,10,11	ACTS.	4:1-22
20	NEH.	12,13	ACTS.	4:23-37
21	ESTHER.	1,2,3	ACTS.	5:1-16
22	ESTHER.	4,5,6	ACTS.	5:17-42
23	ESTHER.	7-10	ACTS.	6
24	JOB.	1,2,3	ACTS.	7:1-19
25	JOB.	4,5,6	ACTS.	7:20-43
26	JOB.	7,8,9	ACTS.	7:44-60
27	JOB.	10,11,12	ACTS.	8:1-25
28	JOB.	13,14,15	ACTS.	8:26-40
29	JOB.	16,17,18	ACTS.	9:1-22
30	JOB.	19,20	ACTS.	9:23-43

JULY

DATE	MORNING		EVENING	
1	JOB.	21,22	ACTS.	10:1-23
2	JOB.	23,24,25	ACTS.	10:24-48
3	JOB.	26,27,28	ACTS.	11
4	JOB.	29,30	ACTS.	12
5	JOB.	31,32	ACTS.	13:1-23
6	JOB.	33,34	ACTS.	13:24-52
7	JOB.	35,36,37	ACTS.	14
8	JOB.	38,39	ACTS.	15:1-21
9	JOB.	40,41,42	ACTS.	15:22-41
10	PS.	1,2,3	ACTS.	16:1-15
11	PS.	4,5,6	ACTS.	16:16-40
12	PS.	7,8,9	ACTS.	17:1-15
13	PS.	10,11,12	ACTS.	17:16-34
14	PS.	13-16	ACTS.	18
15	PS.	17,18	ACTS.	19:1-20
16	PS.	19,20,21	ACTS.	19:21-41
17	PS.	22,23,24	ACTS.	20:1-16
18	PS.	25,26,27	ACTS.	20:17-38
19	PS.	28,29,30	ACTS.	21:1-14
20	PS.	31,32,33	ACTS.	21:15-40
21	PS.	34,35	ACTS.	22
22	PS.	36,37	ACTS.	23:1-11
23	PS.	38,39,40	ACTS.	23:12-35
24	PS.	41,42,43	ACTS.	24
25	PS.	44,45,46	ACTS.	25
26	PS.	47.48.49	ACTS.	26
27	PS.	50,51,52	ACTS.	27:1-25
28	PS.	53,54,55	ACTS.	27:26-44
29	PS.	56,57,58	ACTS.	28:1-15
30	PS.	59,60,61	ACTS.	28:16-31
31	PS.	62,63,64	ROM.	1

SEPTEMBER

DATE	MORNING		EVENING	
1	PS.	148-150	I COR.	11:16-34
2	PROV.	1,2	I COR.	12
3	PROV.	3,4	I COR.	13
4	PROV.	5,6	I COR.	14:1-20
5	PROV.	7,8	I COR.	14:21-40
6	PROV.	9,10	I COR.	15:1-32
7	PROV.	11,12	I COR.	15:33-58
8	PROV.	13,14	I COR.	16
9	PROV.	15,16	II COR.	1
10	PROV.	17,18	II COR.	2
11	PROV.	19,20	II COR.	3
12	PROV.	21,22	II COR.	4
13	PROV.	23,24	II COR.	5
14	PROV.	25,26,27	II COR.	6
15	PROV.	28,29	II COR.	7
16	PROV.	30,31	II COR.	8
17	ECCLES.	1,2,3	II COR.	9
18	ECCLES.	4,5,6	II COR.	10
19	ECCLES.	7,8,9	II COR.	11:1-15
20	ECCLES.	10,11,12	II COR.	11:16-33
21	SOL.	1,2,3	II COR.	12
22	SOL.	4,5	II COR.	13
23	SOL.	6,7,8	GAL.	1
24	ISA.	1,2,3	GAL.	2
25	ISA.	4,5,6	GAL.	`3
26	ISA.	7,8,9	GAL.	4
27	ISA.	10,11,12	GAL.	5
28	ISA.	13,14,15	GAL.	6
29	ISA.	16,17,18	EPH.	1
30	ISA.	19,20,21	EPH.	2

AUGUST

DATE	MORNING		EVENING	
1	PS.	65,66,67	ROM.	2
2	PS.	68,69	ROM.	3
3	PS.	70,71,72	ROM.	4
4	PS.	73,74	ROM.	5
5	PS.	75,76,77	ROM.	6
6	PS.	78	ROM.	7
7	PS.	79,80,81	ROM.	8:1-18
8	PS.	82,83,84	ROM.	8:19-39
9	PS.	85,86,87	ROM.	9
10	PS.	88,89	ROM.	10
11	PS.	90,91,92	ROM.	11:1-21
12	PS.	93,94,95	ROM.	11:22-36
13	PS.	96,97,98	ROM.	12
14	PS.	99-102	ROM.	13
15	PS.	103,104	ROM.	14
16	PS.	105,106	ROM.	15:1-20
17	PS.	107,108	ROM.	15:21-33
18	PS.	109,110,111	ROM.	16
19	PS.	112-115	I COR.	1
20	PS.	116-118	I COR.	2
21	PS.	119:1-48	I COR.	3
22	PS.	119:49-104	I COR.	4
23	PS.	119:105-176	I COR.	5
24	PS.	120-123	I COR.	6
25	PS.	124-127	I COR.	7:1-24
26	PS.	128-131	I COR.	7:25-40
27	PS.	132-135	I COR.	8
28	PS.	136-138	I COR.	9
29	PS.	139-141	I COR.	10:1-13
30	PS.	142-144	I COR.	10:14-33
31	PS.	145-147	I COR.	11:1-15

OCTOBER

DATE	MORNING		EVENING	
1	ISA.	22,23	EPH.	3
2	ISA.	24,25,26	EPH.	4
3	ISA.	27,28	EPH.	5
4	ISA.	29,30	EPH.	6
5	ISA.	31,32,33	PHIL.	1
6	ISA.	34,35,36	PHIL.	2
7	ISA.	37,38	PHIL.	3
8	ISA.	39,40	PHIL.	4
9	ISA.	41,42	COL.	1
10	ISA.	43,44	COL.	2
11	ISA.	45,46,47	COL.	3
12	ISA.	48,49	COL.	4
13	ISA.	50,51,52	I THESS.	1
14	ISA.	53,54,55	I THESS.	2
15	ISA.	56,57,58	I THESS.	3
16	ISA.	59,60,61	I THESS.	4
17	ISA.	62,63,64	I THESS.	5
18	ISA.	65,66	II THESS.	1
19	JER.	1,2	II THESS.	2
20	JER.	3,4	II THESS.	3
21	JER.	5,6	I TIM.	1
22	JER.	7,8	I TIM.	2
23	JER.	9,10	I TIM.	3
24	JER.	11,12,13	I TIM.	4
25	JER.	14,15,16	I TIM.	5
26	JER.	17,18,19	I TIM.	6
27	JER.	20,21,22	II TIM.	1
28	JER.	23,24	II TIM.	2
29	JER.	25,26	II TIM.	3
30	JER.	27,28	II TIM.	4
31	JER.	29,30	TITUS.	1

DATE	MORNING		EVENING		DATE	MORNING		EVENING	
1	JER.	31,32	TITUS.	2	1	EZEK.	45,46	II PET.	3
2	JER.	33,34,35	TITUS.	3	2	EZEK.	47,48	I JOHN.	1
3	JER.	36,37	PHILEM.		3	DAN.	1,2	I JOHN.	2
4	JER.	38,39	HEB.	1	4	DAN.	3,4	I JOHN.	3
5	JER.	40,41,42	HEB.	2	5	DAN.	5,6	I JOHN.	4
6	JER.	43,44,45	HEB.	3	6	DAN.	7,8	I JOHN.	5
7	JER.	46,47,48	HEB.	4	7	DAN.	9,10	II JOHN.	
8	JER.	49,50	HEB.	5	8	DAN.	11,12	III JOHN.	
9	JER.	51,52	HEB.	6	9	HOS.	1-4	JUDE.	
10	LAM.	1,2	HEB.	7	10	HOS.	5-8	REV.	1
11	LAM.	3,4,5	HEB.	8	11	HOS.	9,10,11	REV.	2
12	EZEK.	1,2,3	HEB.	9	12	HOS.	12,13,14	REV.	3
13	EZEK.	4,5,6	HEB.	10:1-23	13	JOEL.	1,2,3	REV.	4
14	EZEK.	7,8,9	HEB.	10:24-39	14	AMOS.	1,2,3	REV.	5
15	EZEK.	10,11,12	HEB.	11:1-19	15	AMOS.	4,5,6	REV.	6
16	EZEK.	13,14,15	HEB.	11:20-40	16	AMOS.	7,8,9	REV.	7
17	EZEK.	16	HEB.	12	17	OBAD.		REV.	8
18	EZEK.	17,18,19	HEB.	13	18	JONAH.		REV.	9
19	EZEK.	20,21	JAS.	1	19	MIC.	1,2,3	REV.	10
20	EZEK.	22,23	JAS.	2	20	MIC.	4,5	REV.	11
21	EZEK.	24,25,26	JAS.	3	21	MIC.	6,7	REV.	12
22	EZEK.	27,28	JAS.	4	22	NAH.		REV.	13
23	EZEK.	29,30,31	JAS.	5	23	HAB.		REV.	14
24	EZEK.	32,33	I PET.	1	24	ZEPH.		REV.	15
25	EZEK.	34,35	I PET.	2	25	HAG.		REV.	16
26	EZEK.	36,37	I PET.	3	26	ZECH.	1,2,3	REV.	17
27	EZEK.	38,39	I PET.	4	27	ZECH.	4,5,6	REV.	18
28	EZEK.	40	I PET.	5	28	ZECH.	7,8,9	REV.	19
29	EZEK.	41,42	II PET.	1	29	ZECH.	10,11,12	REV.	20
30	EZEK.	43,44	II PET.	2	30	ZECH.	13,14	REV.	21
					31	MAL.		REV.	22

SCRIPTURE MEMORY REVIEW

Week	Scripture Reference	Week	Scripture Reference
1		27	
2		28	
3		29	
4		30	
5		31	
6		32	
7		33	
8		34	
9		35	
10		36	
11		37	
12		38	
13		39	
14		40	
15		41	
16		42	
17		43	
18		44	
19		45	
20		46	
21		47	
22		48	
23		49	
24		50	
25		51	
26		52	

Additional Verses

QUIET TIME HIGHLIGHTS

Date	Insight

ADDITIONAL AIDS

QUIET TIME HIGHLIGHTS

Date	Insight

QUIET TIME HIGHLIGHTS

Date	Insight

ADDITIONAL AIDS

QUIET TIME HIGHLIGHTS

Date	Insight

CHURCH FRIENDS LIST

Name	Address	Phone No.

NEXT ACT ON MY PART

l   letter
p   phone call
v   personal visit
o   other

ADDITIONAL AIDS

MINISTRY GOALS AND ACTIVITIES
FOR THE MONTH OF_____

SUNDAY	MONDAY	TUESDAY	WEDNESDAY	THURSDAY	FRIDAY	SATURDAY

MINISTRY GOALS AND ACTIVITIES
FOR THE MONTH OF_____

SUNDAY	MONDAY	TUESDAY	WEDNESDAY	THURSDAY	FRIDAY	SATURDAY

ADDITIONAL AIDS

MINISTRY GOALS AND ACTIVITIES
FOR THE MONTH OF_____

SATURDAY				
FRIDAY				
THURSDAY				
WEDNESDAY				
TUESDAY				
MONDAY				
SUNDAY				

MINISTRY GOALS AND ACTIVITIES
FOR THE MONTH OF_____

SUNDAY	MONDAY	TUESDAY	WEDNESDAY	THURSDAY	FRIDAY	SATURDAY

ADDITIONAL AIDS

MINISTRY GOALS AND ACTIVITIES
FOR THE MONTH OF_____

SUNDAY	MONDAY	TUESDAY	WEDNESDAY	THURSDAY	FRIDAY	SATURDAY

MINISTRY GOALS AND ACTIVITIES
FOR THE MONTH OF_____

	SUNDAY	MONDAY	TUESDAY	WEDNESDAY	THURSDAY	FRIDAY	SATURDAY

ADDITIONAL AIDS

MINISTRY GOALS AND ACTIVITIES
FOR THE MONTH OF_____

SUNDAY	MONDAY	TUESDAY	WEDNESDAY	THURSDAY	FRIDAY	SATURDAY

MINISTRY GOALS AND ACTIVITIES
FOR THE MONTH OF_____

SUNDAY	MONDAY	TUESDAY	WEDNESDAY	THURSDAY	FRIDAY	SATURDAY

ADDITIONAL AIDS

MINISTRY GOALS AND ACTIVITIES
FOR THE MONTH OF_____

SUNDAY	MONDAY	TUESDAY	WEDNESDAY	THURSDAY	FRIDAY	SATURDAY

MINISTRY GOALS AND ACTIVITIES
FOR THE MONTH OF_____

SUNDAY	MONDAY	TUESDAY	WEDNESDAY	THURSDAY	FRIDAY	SATURDAY

ADDITIONAL AIDS

MINISTRY GOALS AND ACTIVITIES
FOR THE MONTH OF_____

SUNDAY	MONDAY	TUESDAY	WEDNESDAY	THURSDAY	FRIDAY	SATURDAY

MINISTRY GOALS AND ACTIVITIES
FOR THE MONTH OF_____

SUNDAY	MONDAY	TUESDAY	WEDNESDAY	THURSDAY	FRIDAY	SATURDAY

ADDITIONAL AIDS